Project Directors

Angela Hall	Emma Palmer
Robin Millar	Mary Whitehouse

Author

Philippa Gardom-Hulme

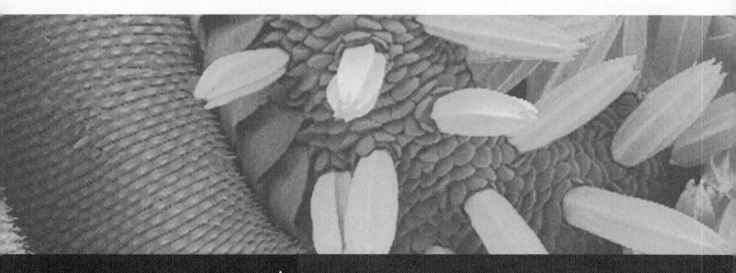

THE UNIVERSITY *of York*

THE SALTERS' INSTITUTE

 Nuffield Foundation

 OCR
RECOGNISING ACHIEVEMENT

OXFORD
UNIVERSITY PRESS

Official Publisher Partnership

OXFORD
UNIVERSITY PRESS

Great Clarendon Street, Oxford OX2 6DP

Oxford University Press is a department of the University of Oxford.
It furthers the University's objective of excellence in research,
scholarship, and education by publishing worldwide in

Oxford   New York

Auckland Cape Town Dar es Salaam Hong Kong Karachi
Kuala Lumpur Madrid Melbourne Mexico City Nairobi
New Delhi Shanghai Taipei Toronto

With offices in
Argentina Austria Brazil Chile Czech Republic France Greece
Guatemala Hungary Italy Japan Poland Portugal Singapore
South Korea Switzerland Thailand Turkey Ukraine Vietnam

Oxford is a registered trade mark of Oxford University Press
in the UK and in certain other countries.

British Library Cataloguing in Publication Data.

Data available.

ISBN 978-0-19-913824-1

10 9 8 7 6 5 4 3

Printed in Great Britain by Bell and Bain Ltd, Glasgow.

Paper used in the production of this book is a natural, recyclable product
made from wood grown in sustainable forests. The manufacturing process
conforms to the environmental regulations of the country of origin.

Acknowledgements
Illustrations by IFA Design, Plymouth, UK, Clive Goodyer, and Q2A Media.

Author acknowledgements
Many thanks to Catherine and Sarah for checking the puzzles, and to
Barney for his inspirational ideas. Thanks to Ruth for her careful editing,
and to Les, Sophie, and Barry at OUP for all their help and patience.

Contents

Introduction

About this book

Welcome to the Twenty-First Century Additional Science Revision Guide! This book will help you prepare for all your GCSE Additional Science module tests. There is one section for each of the biology, chemistry, and physics modules B4–P6, as well as six sections covering Ideas about science. Each section includes several types of pages to help you revise.

Workout: These are to help you find out what you can remember already, and get you thinking about the topic. They include puzzles, flow charts, and lots of other types of questions. Work through these on your own or with a friend, and write your answers in the book. If you get stuck, look in the Factbank. The index will help you find what you need. Check your answers in the back of the book.

Factbank: The Factbanks summarise information from the module in just a few pages. For B4–P6, the Factbanks are divided into short sections, each linked to different statements in the Specification. The Ideas about science Factbanks are different. They are conversations, covering the ideas you will need to apply in different contexts. Read them aloud with a friend if you want to.

Quickfire: Sections B4–P6 each have one page of Quickfire questions. These are short questions that cover most of the content of the module. For some questions, there is space to answer in the book. For others, you will need to use paper or an exercise book.

GCSE-style questions: These are like the questions in the module tests. You could work through them using the Factbank to check things as you go, or do them under test conditions. The answers are in the back of the book. Each section for B4–P6 has one 6-mark question, designed to test your ability to organise ideas, and write in clear and correct English. Use these to help you practise for this type of question in the module tests.

In every section, content covered at Higher-tier only is shown like this.

Other help: The pages at the front of this book include vital revision tips and hints to help you work out what questions are telling you to do. Don't skip these!

Making the most of revision

Remember, remember: You probably won't remember much if you just read this book. Here are some suggestions to help you revise effectively.

Plan your time Work out how many days there are before your test. Then make a timetable so you know which topics to revise when. Include some time off.

Revise actively, don't just read the Factbanks. Highlight key points, scribble extra details in the margin or on Post-it notes, and make up ways to help you remember things. The messier the Factbanks are by the time you take your tests, the better!

Mind maps: try making mind maps to summarise the information in a Factbank. Start with an important idea in the middle. Use arrows to link this to key facts, examples, and other science ideas.

Test yourself on key facts and ideas. Use the Quickfire sections in this book, or get a friend to ask you questions. You could make revision cards, too. Write a question on one side, and the answer on the other. Then test yourself.

Try making up songs or rhymes to help you remember things. You could make up **mnemonics**, too, like this one for the gases in the Earth's atmosphere:

Never **O**ffend **A** Cockroach.

Apply your knowledge: Don't forget you will need to apply knowledge to different contexts, and evaluate data and opinions. The GCSE-style questions in this book give lots of opportunities to practise these skills. Your teacher may give you past test papers, too.

Ideas about science: should not be ignored. These are vital. In your module tests, there could be questions on any of the Ideas about science you have covered so far, set in the context of most of the topics you have covered.

Take short breaks: take plenty of breaks during revision – about 10 minutes an hour works for most people. It's best not to sit still and relax in your breaks – go for a walk, or do some sport. You'll be surprised at what you can remember when you come back, and at how much fresher your brain feels!

Answering exam questions

Read the question carefully, and find the command word. Then look carefully at the information in the question, and at any data. How will they help you answer the question? Use the number of answer lines and the number of marks to help you work out how much detail the examiner wants.

Then write your answer. Make it easy for the examiner to read and understand. If a number needs units, don't forget to include them.

Six-mark questions

Follow the steps below to gain the full six marks:
- Work out exactly what the question is asking.
- Jot down key words to help your answer.
- Organise the key words. You might need to group them into advantages and disadvantages, or sequence them to describe a series of steps.
- Write your answer. Use the organised key words to help.
- Check and correct your spelling, punctuation, and grammar.

Below are examiner's comments on two answers to the question: *"Outline the arguments for and against recycling metals such as aluminium, compared to extracting them from their ores."*

✎ The quality of written communication will be assessed.

Command words

Calculate Work out a number. Use your calculator if you like. You may need to use an equation.
Compare Write about the ways in which two things are the same, and how they are different.
Describe Write a detailed answer that covers what happens, when it happens, and where it happens. Your answer must include facts, or characteristics.
Discuss Write about the issues, giving arguments for and against something, or showing the difference between ideas, opinions, and facts.
Estimate Suggest a rough value, without doing a complete calculation. Use your science knowledge to suggest a sensible answer.
Explain Write a detailed answer that says how and why things happen. Give mechanisms and reasons.
Evaluate You will be given some facts, data, or an article. Write about these, and give your own conclusion or opinion on them.
Justify Give some evidence or an explanation to tell the examiner why you gave an answer.
Outline Give only the key facts, or the steps of a process in the correct order.
Predict Look at the data and suggest a sensible value or outcome. Use trends in the data and your science knowledge to help you.
Show Write down the details, steps, or calculations to show how to get an answer you have been given.
Suggest Apply something you have learnt to a new context, or to come up with a reasonable answer. *Write down* Give a short answer. There is no need for an argument to support your answer.

Answer	Examiners' comments
Alluminnium is expensive and uses lots of emergy too get it. So it is better to resicle it but you cood get it from the ground and youse electrisity but it needs lots of electrisity. And my dad says he cant be bovvered to recycle his cans.	**Grade G** answer: this makes some correct points. However, the points are not well organised and it is not clear which arguments are for and which against recycling metals. There are mistakes of spelling, grammar, and punctuation.
Extracting aluminium from its ore requires much electrical energy. The process produces carbon dioxide (a greenhouse gas) and red mud waste, which damages the environment. There is only a limited amount of aluminium ore in the world, so once it is used up there will be none for people in future. *On the other hand, recycling aluminium requires less energy. If we recycle, there will be more aluminium ore left for future generations, so it is more sustainable to recycle. Some people think recycling is a nuisance, but in my opinion it is worth the extra effort.*	**Grade A/A*** answer: the arguments are made clearly and are organised logically. The candidate has referred to the idea of sustainability. The spelling, punctuation and grammar are faultless.

Equations, units, and data

Equations

You might need to use these equations in the exam. They will be on the exam paper, so you do not need to learn them off by heart.

P4 Explaining motion

$$\text{Speed} = \frac{\text{distance}}{\text{time}}$$

$$\text{Acceleration} = \frac{\text{change in velocity}}{\text{time taken}}$$

$$\text{Momentum} = \text{mass} \times \text{velocity}$$

Change of momentum
$$= \text{resultant force} \times \text{time for which it acts}$$

Work done by a force
$$= \text{force} \times \text{distance moved in direction of force}$$

Energy transferred $= \text{work done}$

Change in gravitational potential energy
$$= \text{weight} \times \text{height}$$

Kinetic energy $= \frac{1}{2} \times \text{mass} \times \text{velocity}^2$

P5 Electric circuits

Power $= \text{voltage} \times \text{current}$

$$\text{Resistance} = \frac{\text{voltage}}{\text{current}}$$

ⓗ
$$\frac{\text{Voltage across primary coil}}{\text{voltage across secondary coil}}$$
$$= \frac{\text{number of turns in primary coil}}{\text{number of turns in secondary coil}}$$

C6 Chemical synthesis

$$\text{Percentage yield} = \frac{\text{actual yield}}{\text{theoretical yield}} \times 100\%$$

P6 Radioactive materials

$E = mc^2$
(E = energy, m = mass lost, c = speed of light in a vacuum)

Units

Length: metres (m), kilometres (km), centimetres (cm), millimetres (mm), micrometres (μm), nanometres (nm)

Mass: kilograms (kg), grams (g), milligrams (mg)

Time: seconds (s), milliseconds (ms), hours (h)

Temperature: degrees Celsius (°C)

Area: cm^2, m^2

Volume: cm^3, dm^3, m^3, litres (l), millilitres (ml)

Speed and **velocity:** m/s, km/s, km/h

Energy: joules (J), kilojoules (kJ), megajoules (MJ), kilowatt-hours (kWh), megawatt-hours (MWh)

Electric current: amperes (A), milliamperes (mA)

Potential difference/voltage: volts (V)

Resistance: ohms (Ω)
Power: watts (W), kilowatts (kW), megawatt (MW)

Radiation dose: sieverts (Sv)

Data

You will be given these data in an examination. You do not need to learn them.

P4 Explaining motion

A mass of 1 kg has a weight of 10 N on the surface of the Earth.

C5 Chemicals of the natural environment

Dry air is made up of approximately 78% nitrogen, 21% oxygen, 1% argon, and 0.04% carbon dioxide.

P5 Electric circuits

Mains supply voltage is 230 V.

ⓗ Module P6 radioactive materials

Speed of light = 300 000 000 m/s

Chemical formulae

Module C4 Chemical patterns

Name	Formula
water	H_2O
hydrogen	H_2
chlorine	Cl_2
bromine	Br_2
iodine	I_2
lithium chloride	LiCl
sodium chloride	NaCl
potassium chloride	KCl
lithium bromide	LiBr
sodium bromide	NaBr
potassium bromide	KBr
lithium iodide	LiI
sodium iodide	NaI
potassium iodide	KI

Module C5 Chemicals of the natural environment

nitrogen	N_2
oxygen	O_2
argon	Ar
carbon dioxide	CO_2
sodium chloride	NaCl
magnesium chloride	$MgCl_2$
sodium sulfate	Na_2SO_4
magnesium sulfate	$MgSO_4$
potassium chloride	KCl
potassium bromide	KBr

Module C6 Chemical synthesis

chlorine	Cl_2
hydrogen	H_2
nitrogen	N_2
oxygen	O_2
hydrochloric acid	HCl
sulfuric acid	H_2SO_4
nitric acid	HNO_3
sodium hydroxide	NaOH
sodium chloride	NaCl

sodium carbonate	$NaCO_3$
sodium nitrate	$NaNO_3$
sodium sulfate	Na_2SO_4
potassium chloride	KCl
magnesium oxide	MgO
magnesium hydroxide	$Mg(OH)_2$
magnesium carbonate	$MgCO_3$
magnesium chloride	$MgCl_2$
magnesium sulfate	$MgSO_4$
calcium carbonate	$CaCO_3$
calcium chloride	$CaCl_2$
calcium sulfate	$CaSO_4$

Test for ions

Tests for positive ions

Ion	Test	Observation
calcium Ca^{2+}	add dilute sodium hydroxide solution	white precipitate, insoluble in excess sodium hydroxide solution
copper Cu^{2+}	add dilute sodium hydroxide solution	blue precipitate
iron(II) Fe^{2+}	add dilute sodium hydroxide solution	green precipitate
iron(III) Fe^{3+}	add dilute sodium hydroxide solution	red-brown precipitate
zinc Zn^{2+}	add dilute sodium hydroxide solution	white precipitate, soluble in excess sodium hydroxide solution

Tests for negative ions

Ion	Test	Observation
carbonate CO_3^{2-}	add dilute acid	fizzes, carbon dioxide gas produced
chloride Cl^-	add dilute nitric acid, then silver nitrate solution	white precipitate
bromide Br^-	add dilute nitric acid, then silver nitrate solution	cream precipitate
iodide I^-	add dilute nitric acid, then silver nitrate solution	yellow precipitate
sulfate SO_4^{2-}	add dilute acid, then barium chloride or barium nitrate	white precipitate

Periodic table

Key

relative atomic mass
atomic symbol
name
atomic (proton) number

1	2											3	4	5	6	7	0
							1 **H** hydrogen 1										4 **He** helium 2
7 **Li** lithium 3	9 **Be** beryllium 4											11 **B** boron 5	12 **C** carbon 6	14 **N** nitrogen 7	16 **O** oxygen 8	19 **F** fluorine 9	20 **Ne** neon 10
23 **Na** sodium 11	24 **Mg** magnesium 12											27 **Al** aluminium 13	28 **Si** silicon 14	31 **P** phosphorus 15	32 **S** sulfur 16	35.5 **Cl** chlorine 17	40 **Ar** argon 18
39 **K** potassium 19	40 **Ca** calcium 20	45 **Sc** scandium 21	48 **Ti** titanium 22	51 **V** vanadium 23	52 **Cr** chromium 24	55 **Mn** manganese 25	56 **Fe** iron 26	59 **Co** cobalt 27	59 **Ni** nickel 28	63.5 **Cu** copper 29	65 **Zn** zinc 30	70 **Ga** gallium 31	73 **Ge** germanium 32	75 **As** arsenic 33	79 **Se** selenium 34	80 **Br** bromine 35	84 **Kr** krypton 36
86 **Rb** rubidium 37	88 **Sr** strontium 38	89 **Y** yttrium 39	91 **Zr** zirconium 40	93 **Nb** niobium 41	96 **Mo** molybdenum 42	98 **Tc** technetium 43	101 **Ru** ruthenium 44	103 **Rh** rhodium 45	106 **Pd** palladium 46	108 **Ag** silver 47	112 **Cd** cadmium 48	115 **In** indium 49	119 **Sn** tin 50	122 **Sb** antimony 51	128 **Te** tellurium 52	127 **I** iodine 53	131 **Xe** xenon 54
133 **Cs** caesium 55	137 **Ba** barium 56	139 **La*** lanthanum 57	178 **Hf** hafnium 72	181 **Ta** tantalum 73	184 **W** tungsten 74	186 **Re** rhenium 75	190 **Os** osmium 76	192 **Ir** iridium 77	195 **Pt** platinum 78	197 **Au** gold 79	201 **Hg** mercury 80	204 **Tl** thallium 81	207 **Pb** lead 82	209 **Bi** bismuth 83	[209] **Po** polonium 84	[210] **At** astatine 85	[222] **Rn** radon 86
[223] **Fr** francium 87	[226] **Ra** radium 88	[227] **Ac*** actinium 89	[261] **Rf** rutherfordium 104	[262] **Db** dubnium 105	[266] **Sg** seaborgium 106	[264] **Bh** bohrium 107	[277] **Hs** hassium 108	[268] **Mt** meitnerium 109	[271] **Ds** damstadtium 110	[272] **Rg** roentgenium 111							

Elements with atomic numbers 112–116 have been reported but not fully authenticated

The lanthanoids (atomic numbers 58–71) and the actinoids (atomic numbers 90–103) have been omitted.

1 Use words from the box below to label the cell diagrams.

nucleus	cytoplasm	cell membrane	mitochondrion
cell wall	chloroplast	circular DNA	vacuole

a

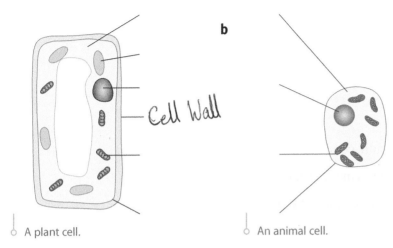

Cell Wall

A plant cell.

b

An animal cell.

c

A bacterial cell.

d

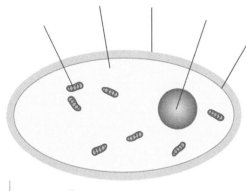

A yeast cell.

2 The stages opposite show how an enzyme catalyses a reaction at its active site.

The reaction involves breaking down one molecule to make two smaller molecules.

Write the letters of the stages in the correct order in the boxes below.

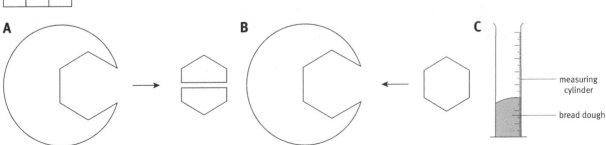

A   B   C

measuring cylinder

bread dough

3 The graph shows the link between pH and rate of reaction for two different reactions that are controlled by enzymes.

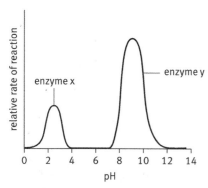

a Which enzyme works best in acidic conditions? _____

b What is the pH range in which enzyme X is active? _____

c Would enzyme Y work in a human stomach? Explain your answer.

_____

4 Gareth set up the investigation below.

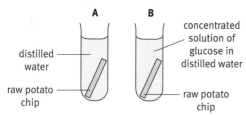

Write the letter of one or more test tubes next to each statement below.

a This chip gets bigger. _____

b This chip feels firmer when it is taken out of the test tube. _____

c Overall, more water has moved from the surrounding liquid into the chip. _____

d Overall, more water has moved out of the chip into the surrounding liquid. _____

e Water gets into and out of the potato by diffusion. _____

f Water gets into and out of the potato by osmosis through cell membranes. _____

B4.1.1, B4.1.4 Why are there chemical reactions in cells?

All living things carry out seven **life processes**. Living things move, reproduce, sense their surroundings, grow, excrete waste products, and need nutrition.

These processes depend on chemical reactions which happen in cells. Many of the reactions need energy. This energy is released by the seventh life process – **respiration**. Respiration is a series of chemical reactions that releases energy by breaking down large food molecules in all living cells.

B4.1.5–7 What are enzymes?

Enzymes speed up chemical reactions in cells. An enzyme is a natural **catalyst**. Catalysts speed up chemical reactions without getting used up.

Enzymes are proteins. They are made in cells. In cells, genes carry the instructions to make enzymes.

Every reaction in a cell needs its own enzyme. The reacting molecules must fit exactly into the **active site** of the enzyme. So every enzyme has its own shape. This is the **lock and key model**.

B4.1.8–11 What conditions do enzymes need?

Enzymes work best at their **optimum temperature**.
- Below the optimum temperature, reactions are slow.
- If the temperature is too high, an enzyme changes its shape. It no longer catalyses its reactions.

(H) The enzyme has been **denatured**.

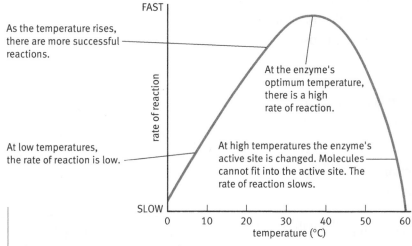

FAST

As the temperature rises, there are more successful reactions.

rate of reaction

At the enzyme's optimum temperature, there is a high rate of reaction.

At low temperatures, the rate of reaction is low.

At high temperatures the enzyme's active site is changed. Molecules cannot fit into the active site. The rate of reaction slows.

SLOW

temperature (°C)

The graph shows how the rate of an enzyme-catalysed reaction changes with temperature.

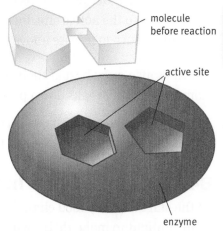

1 An enzyme has an active site.

molecule before reaction

active site

enzyme

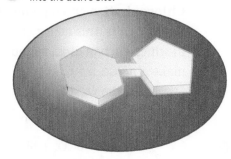

2 Only the correct molecule fits into the active site.

3 The reaction takes place in the active site.

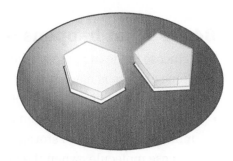

4 The product leaves the active site. The enzyme can be used again.

product molecules

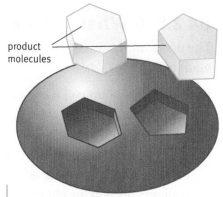

The lock-and-key model of enzyme function.

(H) An enzyme's activity at different temperatures is a balance between:
- increasing reaction rates as temperature increases
- changes to the active site, including denaturing, as the temperature increases above the optimum.

Enzymes also work best at their optimum pH. For example, in the stomach, pepsin breaks down proteins most efficiently at pH 2.

(H) At other pH values, the shape of pepsin's active site changes. The protein molecules it breaks down no longer fit into its active site.

B4.1.2–3, B4.2.1–2 What is photosynthesis?

At the start of every food chain is a plant. Plants use energy from sunlight to make their own food by **photosynthesis**. Photosynthesis happens like this:
- **Chlorophyll**, a green pigment, absorbs light energy.
- In plant cells, this energy brings about a series of reactions in which carbon dioxide and water molecules join together to make glucose, a sugar.
- Oxygen is the waste product of the reactions.

$$\text{carbon dioxide} + \text{water} \xrightarrow{\text{light energy}} \text{glucose} + \text{oxygen}$$

(H)
$$6CO_2 + 6H_2O \xrightarrow{\text{light energy}} C_6H_{12}O_6 + 6O_2$$

Photosynthesis also happens in some microorganisms, for example, in phytoplankton.

B4.2.4 What happens to the glucose?

The glucose made in photosynthesis has three main uses:
- Some glucose is made into the chemicals that plant cells need to grow, for example, chlorophyll, proteins, and **cellulose**.
- Some glucose molecules join together to make starch molecules. Starch is a storage chemical. It breaks down into glucose molecules when the plant needs more glucose.
- Some glucose is used in respiration.

B4.2.5–6 What's in a plant cell?

The diagram shows the structure of a typical plant cell.

Each part of a plant cell has a vital function:
- **Chloroplasts** contain chlorophyll, and the enzymes for photosynthesis.
- The **nucleus** contains DNA. This carries the genetic code for making enzymes and other proteins needed for photosynthesis.

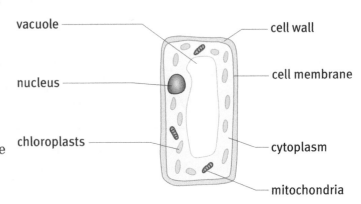

vacuole

nucleus

chloroplasts

cell wall

cell membrane

cytoplasm

mitochondria

B
4

- Enzymes and other proteins are made in the **cytoplasm**.
- The **cell membrane** lets gas and water molecules into the cell, but stops chemicals with bigger molecules getting out.
- Respiration happens in **mitochondria**.
- The **vacuole** contains glucose molecules, dissolved in water.
- The **cell wall** is rigid. It is made of cellulose.

B4.2.7–13 How do chemicals get into cells?

Molecules get into and out of cells by **diffusion**. In diffusion, molecules move from a region of higher concentration to a region of their lower concentration. Diffusion is a passive process – it does not need extra energy.

Carbon dioxide molecules diffuse into leaves through tiny pores. Oxygen molecules diffuse out of leaves through these same pores.

Water gets into and out of a cell through its **partially permeable membrane**. Small molecules can get through the membrane, but bigger ones cannot. Water molecules diffuse through the membrane from a dilute solution (where there are more water molecules) to a more concentrated solution (where there are fewer.) This type of diffusion is **osmosis**. Water moves into root cells by osmosis.

Plants take in minerals such as nitrates through root cells. They use nitrogen atoms from nitrates to make proteins.

Ⓗ **Active transport** moves nitrate ions across cell membranes. Energy from respiration helps transport the particles from a region of lower concentration outside the cell to a region of higher concentration inside the cell. The diagrams summarise active transport.

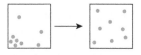

In diffusion, particles spread out from where there are lots of them to where there are fewer of them.

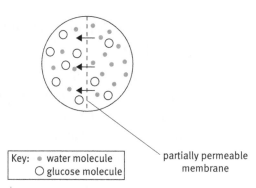

Key: • water molecule
      ○ glucose molecule

partially permeable membrane

In osmosis, water molecules move through a partially permeable membrane.

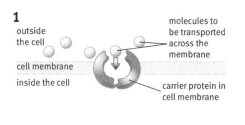

1

outside the cell

molecules to be transported across the membrane

cell membrane

inside the cell

carrier protein in cell membrane

2

Energy from respiration is used to change the shape of the carrier protein.

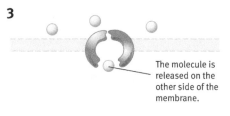

3

The molecule is released on the other side of the membrane.

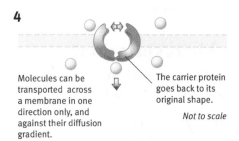

4

Molecules can be transported across a membrane in one direction only, and against their diffusion gradient.

The carrier protein goes back to its original shape.

Not to scale

In active transport, cells use energy to transport molecules across the membrane.

B4.2.14–15 What speeds up photosynthesis?

The rate of photosynthesis depends on several factors, including:

- **Temperature** – photosynthesis is faster at higher temperatures.
- **Carbon dioxide concentration** – increasing this speeds up photosynthesis.
- **Light intensity** – at low light levels, increasing the amount of light increases the rate of photosynthesis. But above a certain point, increasing the amount of light no longer increases the rate of photosynthesis. Some other factor, for example, carbon dioxide concentration, now limits the rate. This is the **limiting factor**.

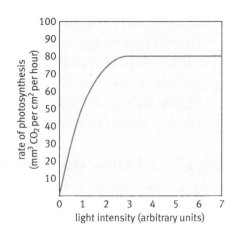

B4.2.16–17 How can we investigate plants and light?

Different plants are adapted to different light levels. You can investigate the plants in different habitats using:

- a **light meter** to measure light intensity
- a **quadrat** (placed at random) and **identification key** to survey the plants in a square metre.

To investigate how plant species change gradually from one area to another, take samples at intervals along a straight line, or **transect**.

B4.3.1–2 Why do living organisms need energy?

Living organisms use energy from respiration for some chemical reactions in cells, including those involved in:

- movement
- ⒣ active transport
- synthesising (making) big molecules, including:
  - polymers (such as starch and cellulose) from glucose in plants
  - amino acids (from glucose and nitrates) to make proteins in plant, animal, and microbial cells.

B4.3.3–5 What is aerobic respiration?

Aerobic respiration releases energy. It happens in plant and animal cells, and in some microorganisms. It needs oxygen.

$$\text{glucose} + \text{oxygen} \longrightarrow \text{carbon dioxide} + \text{water}$$

⒣
$$C_6H_{12}O_6 + 6O_2 \longrightarrow 6CO_2 + 6H_2O$$

B4.3.6–9, 4.3.12 What is anaerobic respiration?

Anaerobic respiration releases less energy per glucose molecule than aerobic respiration. It happens in plant and animal cells, and in some microorganisms, when there is little or no oxygen, for example:

- in plant roots, when the soil is waterlogged
- in bacteria, in deep puncture wounds
- in human muscle cells during vigorous exercise.

This equation summarises anaerobic respiration in animal cells, and in some bacteria:

$$\text{glucose} \longrightarrow \text{lactic acid}$$

In plant cells, and in some microorganisms such as yeast, anaerobic respiration forms different products:

$$\text{glucose} \longrightarrow \text{ethanol} + \text{carbon dioxide}$$

Anaerobic respiration in yeast produces carbon dioxide, which makes bread rise. The process also makes ethanol, for alcoholic drinks.

Some bacteria produce methane gas when they break down organic materials such as manure. This **biogas** is a useful fuel.

B4.3.10–11 What's in a cell?

The diagrams show the structures of animal, bacteria, and yeast cells.

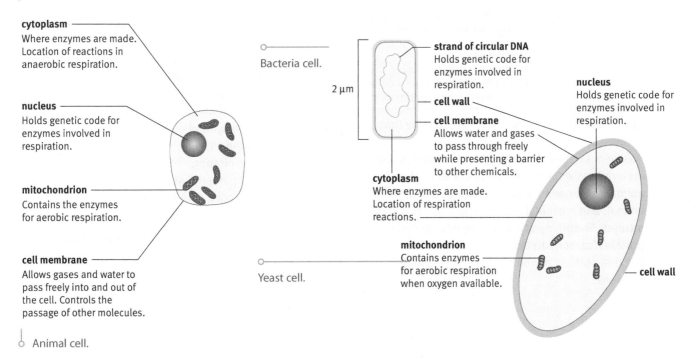

cytoplasm
Where enzymes are made. Location of reactions in anaerobic respiration.

nucleus
Holds genetic code for enzymes involved in respiration.

mitochondrion
Contains the enzymes for aerobic respiration.

cell membrane
Allows gases and water to pass freely into and out of the cell. Controls the passage of other molecules.

Animal cell.

Bacteria cell.

2 μm

strand of circular DNA
Holds genetic code for enzymes involved in respiration.

cell wall

cell membrane
Allows water and gases to pass through freely while presenting a barrier to other chemicals.

cytoplasm
Where enzymes are made. Location of respiration reactions.

Yeast cell.

nucleus
Holds genetic code for enzymes involved in respiration.

mitochondrion
Contains enzymes for aerobic respiration when oxygen available.

cell wall

Use extra paper to answer these questions if you need to.

1 List the seven processes of life.

2 Write **T** next to the statements below that are true. Write corrected versions of the statements that are false.
   a The waste product of photosynthesis is carbon dioxide.
   b In aerobic respiration, glucose and oxygen react together to make carbon dioxide and water.
   c Anaerobic respiration releases more energy per glucose molecule than aerobic respiration.
   d Enzymes are carbohydrates that speed up chemical reactions.
   e Photosynthesis happens in plant and phytoplankton cells.

3 Copy and complete the word equations below.
   a Photosynthesis:
      carbon dioxide + water ⟶ ___ + ___
   b Aerobic respiration:
      glucose + ___ ⟶ ___ + ___
   c Anaerobic respiration in animal cells:
      glucose ⟶ ___
   d Anaerobic respiration in yeast and plant cells:
      glucose ⟶ ___ + ___

4 Match each word to its definition.

Word	Definition
diffusion	making a chemical with bigger particles from ones with smaller particles
osmosis	movement of molecules from a region of their higher concentration to one of their lower concentration
synthesis	movement of water through a partially permeable membrane to a region of their higher concentration to one of their lower concentration

5 In each pair of bold words, highlight the one that is correct.
   Polymers such as **starch/oxygen** and **water/cellulose** are synthesised from **glucose/nitrates** in **plant/ animal** cells. Amino acids are synthesised in plant, animal, and microbial cells from glucose and **starch/ nitrates**. The amino acids join together to make **proteins/carbohydrates**.

6 List three places in which anaerobic respiration happens.

7 Kish measures the rate of an enzyme-catalysed reaction at different temperatures. His results are on the graph below.

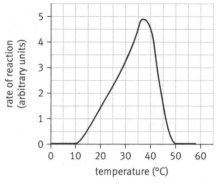

   a What is the rate of reaction at 20 °C?
   b What is the optimum temperature for the enzyme?
   c Over what range of temperatures does the enzyme catalyse the reaction?
   d Why does the enzyme not catalyse the reaction above a certain temperature?

8 A scientist recorded the rate of photosynthesis of a plant over 24 hours. She plotted her results on the graph below.

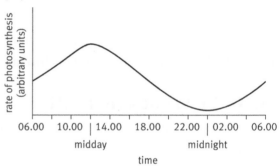

   a At what time was the rate of photosynthesis lowest?
   b At what time was there the highest concentration of oxygen in the air just around the leaves?
   c At what time was most carbon dioxide being removed from the air?

H 9 Write balanced symbol equations to summarise:
   a photosynthesis
   b aerobic respiration.

10 Copy and complete the sentences below. Use words from this list: roots, respiration, nitrates, energy.
   In active transport, chemicals such as _____ are absorbed by plant _____. The process requires _____. This comes from the process of _____.

1 Riana investigates anaerobic respiration in yeast.

She mixes yeast with sugar and warm water.

After 10 minutes, she adds the yeast mixture to flour, and kneads the dough.

She then sets up the apparatus opposite.

Riana measures the height of the dough every 5 minutes for 25 minutes.

The temperature of the room was 24 °C.

Her results are in the table.

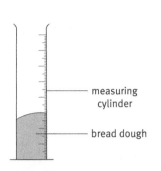
measuring cylinder

bread dough

Time (min)	Height of dough (cm)
0	5
5	10
10	13
15	15
20	16
25	16

a   Describe the pattern shown by the results.

_____

_____ [2]

b   Riana discusses the investigation with other students.

Here are their ideas.

Zita
The higher the temperature, the faster the dough will rise.

Tom
The dough would rise faster if you added alkali to the mixture of yeast, sugar, and water to increase the pH.

Sam
The dough would rise faster if you put it under a lamp.

i   Is Zita's idea correct? Explain your answer.

_____

_____

_____ [3]

Exam tip

When you are asked to explain an answer, make sure you give detailed reasons to back up your response.

ii   Is Sam's idea correct? Explain your answer.

_____

_____ [2]

iii Suggest how Tom could test his idea.
    Include any safety precautions he would need to take, and the results he would expect if his idea was correct.

_____

_____

_____

_____ [4]

c   Write a word equation for the anaerobic respiration reaction that happens in yeast.

_____ [1]

d   Draw lines to match each cell structure with its function in respiration.

Structure	Function
nucleus	The enzymes used in aerobic respiration are found here.
cytoplasm	The enzymes used in anaerobic respiration are found here.
mitochondria	The genetic code for making enzymes used in respiration is found here.

[2]

Total [14]

2   Describe and explain how substances move in and out of different types of plant cell by diffusion, including osmosis.

🖊 The quality of written communication will be assessed in your answer to this question.

Write your answer on separate paper or in your exercise book.

Total [6]

3   Artem investigates the effect of light on the rate of photosynthesis.

He sets up the apparatus opposite.

The temperature is 18 °C.

Artem counts the number of bubbles released by the pondweed in one minute.

His results are in the table.

water
pondweed
paper clip
'weight'
lamp

Distance of plant from lamp (cm)	Number of bubbles in one minute			
	Test 1	Test 2	Test 3	Mean
100	10	16	13	13
80	15	18	18	17
60	20	20	23	21
40	35	37	33	35
20	45	49	53	49

a   **i**   Give the range for the number of bubbles when the distance from the lamp was 80 cm.

_____ [1]

ii   Plot the mean results on a graph. Use the axes opposite. [2]

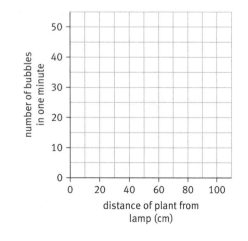

number of bubbles in one minute

distance of plant from lamp (cm)

b Write a conclusion for the investigation.

_____

_____ [2]

c Outline how Artem could use the apparatus above to investigate the effect of temperature on the rate of photosynthesis.

Include the names of any extra pieces of apparatus he would need.

_____

_____

_____ [2]

d **i** Write a word equation to summarise photosynthesis.

_____ [1]

ii Name the structure in a plant cell that contains the enzymes for the reactions in photosynthesis.

_____ [1]

Total [9]

4 Katya and Martha did some fieldwork to investigate the effect of light on plants growing in a wildlife park.

They used a quadrat and an identification key to survey the plants growing in different square-metre sections of the wildlife park.

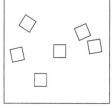 

Katya's quadrats   Martha's quadrats

a Katya and Martha drew diagrams to show where they placed their quadrats. Who was studying a transect? Suggest why she decided to study a transect.

_____

_____

_____ [1]

b The diagrams show what Martha found in three of her quadrats.

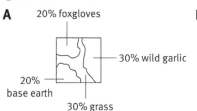  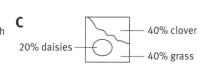

A 20% foxgloves
30% wild garlic
20% base earth
30% grass

B 35% base earth
65% grass

C 40% clover
20% daisies
40% grass

Martha also made some notes from a flower identification key:

Which quadrat above (**A**, **B**, or **C**) is most likely to have been placed under some trees?

Give a reason for your answer.

_____

_____ [1]

Total [2]

Foxglove – likes shade

Clover – grow well in full sunlight

Daisies – like full sunlight

Wild garlic – likes shade

⊕ **Going for the highest grades**

5 Green plants make their own food by photosynthesis.

   a   Write a balanced symbol equation to summarise photosynthesis.

     _____ [2]

   b   The graph shows the relationship between light intensity and the rate of photosynthesis at two different concentrations of carbon dioxide.

     Explain what the graph shows about how two factors – light intensity and carbon dioxide – affect the rate of photosynthesis.
Include ideas about limiting factors in your answer.

     _____

     _____

     _____ [3]

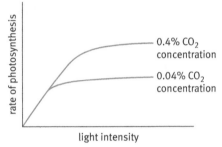

Exam tip

If three marks are available, try to make three points in your answer.

   c   Plants take in nitrates through their roots.

     i   Describe what the nitrates are used for.

       _____

       _____ [2]

     ii Describe how plant root hair cells absorb nitrates.

       _____

       _____

       _____ [5]

Total [2]

1 a Fill in column B of the table below. Choose words from the box.

harmful	toxic	explosive	corrosive
	oxidising	highly flammable	

b In column C, write down one safety precaution you must take when using a chemical that displays the hazard symbol. (Assume you are already wearing eye protection.)

A Hazard symbol	B Meaning of symbol	C Safety precaution
(corrosive symbol)		
(skull and crossbones symbol)		
(flame symbol)		

2 Write the symbol of each element in the box below its proton number. You can find these in the periodic table on page 8.

Proton number	3	26	53	16	9	92	7	16	8	53	16	75	23	53	14	8	7
Symbol	Li					U											

Now crack the code. What does the sentence say?

_____

3 Join the dots to make a picture.

Start at the element with the lowest relative atomic mass. Join this to the element with the next lowest relative atomic mass, and so on.

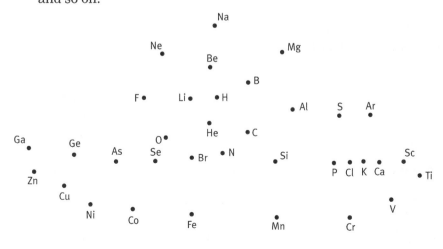

4 Write the symbol of each element in the box below its relative atomic mass. You can find this information in the periodic table on page 8.

Relative atomic mass	32	4	127	32	9	197	48	19	238	7	232	127	14	39
Symbol									U		Th			

Now crack the code. What does the sentence say?

_____

5 On the periodic table:
   • colour in red the group that includes the element calcium
   • colour in blue the period that includes the element phosphorus
   • colour in pencil all the non-metals
   • circle in red **three** elements that form ions with a charge of +1
   • circle in blue **three** elements that form ions with a charge of −1.

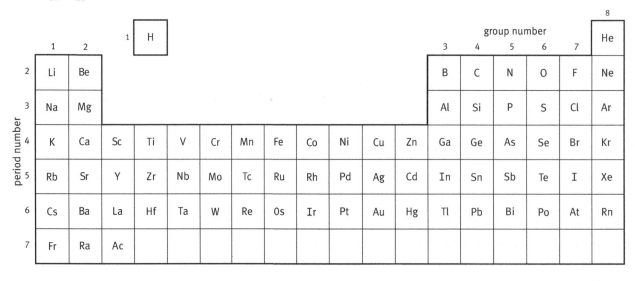

6 Draw crosses on the circles to show how the electrons are arranged in atoms of these elements. (Hint: not all of the shells will contain electrons.)

lithium

beryllium

carbon

fluorine

sodium

phosphorus

chlorine

argon

C4.1.2, C4.1.6–9, C4.2.5 What is the periodic table?

The periodic table is shown on page 8. In the periodic table:
- The elements are arranged in order of **proton number**.
- There are repeating patterns in the element's properties.
- The vertical columns are called **groups**.
- The elements in a group have similar properties.
- The horizontal rows are called **periods**.
- The elements to the left of a stepped line between aluminium and silicon, germanium and arsenic, and so on, are metals. The elements to the right of this stepped line are non-metals.

C4.1.3–5 How was the periodic table created?

In the early 1800s, Döbereiner noticed that there were several groups of three elements with similar properties.

Newlands arranged the elements in order of relative atomic mass. Every eighth element had similar properties. His pattern only worked for the first 16 elements.

Mendeleev showed there were patterns in the properties of all the elements when arranged in relative atomic mass order. He made a sensible pattern by leaving gaps for missing elements. He predicted the missing elements' properties. Later, scientists discovered these elements.

C4.1.18 What do hazard symbols mean?

Symbol	Meaning	Safety precautions Wear eye protection and . . .
	Toxic – can cause death if absorbed by skin, swallowed or breathed in	• wear gloves • work in fume cupboard or wear mask over mouth and nose
	Harmful – like toxic substances, but less dangerous	• wash off spills quickly • use in a well-ventilated room
	Corrosive – attacks surfaces and living tissue, like eyes or skin	• wear gloves
	Explosive	• avoid situations that could initiate an explosion
	Highly flammable – catches fire easily	• keep away from flames, sparks and oxidizing chemicals
	Oxidising – provides oxygen so other chemicals burn more fiercely	• keep away from flammable chemicals

C4.1.11–19, C4.1.28 (part), 29, 30 What are the patterns in the properties of the elements?

Group 1: the alkali metals

The alkali metals include the elements lithium (Li), sodium (Na), and potassium (K). The alkali metals:

- have low densities, so they float on water
- have **low melting** and **boiling points**
- are **shiny** when freshly cut
- quickly **tarnish** in damp air because they react with oxygen.

Alkali metals react with water to make **hydrogen** and an **alkaline solution**.

For example:

$$\text{sodium} + \text{water} \longrightarrow \text{hydrogen} + \text{sodium hydroxide}$$
$$2Na(s) + 2H_2O(l) \longrightarrow H_2(g) + 2NaOH(aq)$$

The symbol equation shows that two atoms of sodium react with two water molecules to make one hydrogen molecule and two formula units of sodium hydroxide.

Going down the group, the reactions get more vigorous.

Alkali metals also react vigorously with **chlorine gas** to make chlorides. The chlorides are **colourless crystalline solids**. Again, the reactions get more vigorous going down the group.

For example:

$$\text{lithium} + \text{chlorine} \longrightarrow \text{lithium chloride}$$
$$2Li(s) + Cl_2(g) \longrightarrow 2LiCl(s)$$

C4.1.20–27, C4.1.28 (Part) Group 7: the halogens

Name and symbol	Formula	State at room temperature	Colour
chlorine, Cl	Cl_2	gas	pale green
bromine, Br	Br_2	liquid	deep red liquid with red-brown vapour
iodine, I	I_2	solid	grey solid with purple vapour

Going down the group, **melting point** and **boiling point** increase.

Halogen molecules are **diatomic** – they are made from two atoms joined together. For example, the formula of bromine is Br_2.

Going **down** group 7, the elements become **less reactive**.
For example:

*   Hot iron glows brightly in chlorine gas. It glows less brightly in bromine, and hardly at all in iodine.

    iron + chlorine $\longrightarrow$ iron chloride

*   James adds pale green chlorine solution to a colourless solution of sodium bromide. Red bromine solution forms. Chlorine is more reactive than bromine, so it displaces bromine from its salt in a **displacement** reaction.

    chlorine + sodium bromide $\longrightarrow$ sodium chloride + bromine

C4.1.1, C4.2.1–4, C4.2.10–14 Explaining patterns in the properties of elements

Particle	Relative mass	Relative charge
proton	1	+1
neutron	1	none
electron	negligible	−1

Atomic structure

An atom has a tiny central nucleus made of **protons** and **neutrons**. Around the nucleus are **electrons**.

All atoms of the same element have the same number of protons. For example, every sodium atom has 11 protons. The **proton number** of sodium is 11.

The number of electrons in an atom is the same as the number of protons. Electrons are arranged in **shells**. Each electron shell fills from left to right across a period.

Exam tip

Practise using the periodic table to work out the number of protons, neutrons, and electrons in atoms.

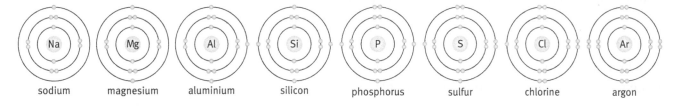

sodium	magnesium	aluminium	silicon	phosphorus	sulfur	chlorine	argon

You can also represent the atomic structure of sodium as 2.8.1.

Every group 1 element has one electron in its outer shell. An element's chemical properties depend on its electron arrangement.
So group 1 elements have similar chemical reactions.

C4.2.6–9 Elements have distinctive flame colours

If you hold any lithium compound in a Bunsen flame at the end of a platinum wire, you see a red flame. The compounds of other elements make different colours.

When the light from the flame goes through a prism, it makes a **line spectrum**.

Every element has a different spectrum. Chemists have studied these spectra and so discovered new elements, for example helium.

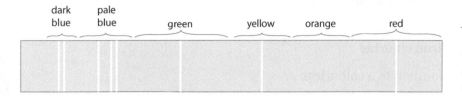

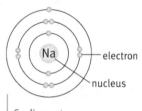

This is the spectrum for helium. The lines are coloured. The series of colours are different for each element.

C4.3.1–3, C4.3.6–9 What are ions and ionic compounds?

If you melt an ionic compound containing metal and non-metal ions, it conducts electricity. Charged particles called **ions** carry the current.

An ion is an atom or group of atoms that has gained or lost electrons. So it has an overall charge.

An atom of sodium has 11 positively charged protons in its nucleus. It has 11 negatively charged electrons. A sodium atom loses one electron to become an ion. A sodium ion has 11 protons and 10 electrons. Its overall charge is +1. Its formula is Na^+.

A chlorine atom has 17 positively charged protons in its nucleus. It has 17 negatively charged electrons. A chlorine atom gains one electron to become an ion. A chloride ion has 17 protons and 18 electrons. Its overall charge is −1. Its formula is Cl^-.

Sodium chloride is a compound that is made from ions. It is **ionic**. Every compound of a group 1 metal with a group 7 metal is ionic.

In solid ionic compounds, the ions are arranged in a regular lattice. So solid ionic compounds form crystals.

When ionic crystals melt or dissolve in water, the ions are free to move independently. So ionic compounds conduct electricity when liquid or in solution.

Sodium atom.

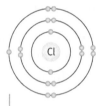

Sodium ion.

Chlorine atom.

Chlorine ion.

C4.3.4–5 Ion calculations

The formula of sodium chloride (common salt) is NaCl. There is one sodium ion for every chloride ion. The total charge on the ions in the formula is zero. So sodium chloride, like all compounds, is electrically neutral.

	Sodium ion	Chloride ion	Sodium chloride
Charges	+1	−1	$(+1) + (-1) = 0$

Working out the formulae of an ionic compound

What is the formula of potassium oxide?

The charge on a potassium ion is +1 (K^+).
The charge on an oxide ion is −2 (O^{2-}).
The total charge on the ions in the formula must equal zero.

So potassium oxide has two K^+ ions for every one O^{2-} ion.

So the formula of potassium oxide is K_2O.

Working out the charge on an ion

The formula of calcium bromide is $CaBr_2$.
The charge on one bromide ion is –1.
What is the charge on the calcium ion?

The total charge on the two bromide ions is $-1 \times 2 = -2$.

The total charge on the ions in the formula must be zero (neutral).

So the charge on the calcium ion is +2.

C4.1.31–33 Balancing equations

Balance the equation $HCl + MgO \longrightarrow MgCl_2 + H_2O$

- Count the number of hydrogen atoms on each side of the arrow. There are one on the left and two on the right. Write a big 2 to the left of HCl:

$$2HCl + MgO \longrightarrow MgCl_2 + H_2O$$

Now there are two hydrogen atoms on each side.

- Count the number of chlorine atoms on each side. The big 2 to the left of HCl means that there are two on the left. There are also two on the right of the arrow (in $MgCl_2$). The number of chlorine atoms is balanced.
- Count the number of magnesium atoms on each side of the arrow. There is one on the left and one on the right.
- Count the number of oxygen atoms on each side of the arrow. There is one on the left and one on the right.
- Add state symbols.

So the balanced equation is:
$2HCl(aq) + MgO(s) \longrightarrow MgCl_2(aq) + H_2O(l)$

Exam tip

Never change the formula of a compound or element to balance an equation.

Use extra paper to answer these questions if you need to.

1 Choose words from the box to fill in the gaps in the sentences below. The words may be used once, more than once, or not at all.

| shells | electrons | nucleus |
| neutrons | 7 | protons | 2 |

Atoms have a small central _____. This is made of protons and _____. Electrons are arranged in _____ round the nucleus. In a neutral atom, the number of _____ is equal to the number of protons. The way an element reacts depends on how its _____ are arranged.

Chlorine, bromine, and iodine are in group _____ of the periodic table. They all have _____ electrons in their outer shell.

2 For the sentences below, write **1** next to each sentence that is true for **group 1**. Write **7** next to each sentence that is true for **group 7**. Write **B** next to each sentence that is true for **both group 1 and group 7**. Use the data in the table to help you.

Element	Boiling point (°C)	Density (g/cm³)
lithium	1342	0.53
sodium	883	0.97
potassium	766	0.86
chlorine	−34	1.56
bromine	58	3.1
iodine	184	4.9

a Going down the group, boiling point increases.
b Going up this group, the elements get more reactive.
c Going up this group, proton number decreases.
d Atoms of the elements in this group form diatomic molecules.
e The elements in this group tarnish quickly in damp air.
f Going down this group, density increases.

3 Complete the word equations.
a sodium + water $\longrightarrow$ sodium hydroxide + _____
b potassium + chlorine $\longrightarrow$ _____ _____
c hydrogen + iodine $\longrightarrow$ _____ _____
d lithium + _____ $\longrightarrow$ lithium hydroxide + _____
e sodium + _____ $\longrightarrow$ _____ chloride
f lithium + _____ $\longrightarrow$ lithium bromide

4 Use the periodic table to work out the number of protons, neutrons, and electrons in atoms of the elements below.
a sodium **b** phosphorus **c** aluminium
d vanadium **e** yttrium

5 Fill in the empty boxes.

6 Decide which of the following pairs of solutions will react together in displacement reactions. Then write word equations for the pairs of solutions that react.

Name	Formula
water	
hydrogen gas	
	KCl
sodium hydroxide	
	I_2
chlorine gas	
potassium bromide	

a chlorine and sodium bromide
b iodine and potassium bromide
c bromine and sodium iodide
d bromine and sodium chloride
e chlorine and potassium iodide

7 Look at the symbol equation below. It summarises the reaction of iron with chlorine to make iron chloride.

$$2Fe + 3Cl_2 \longrightarrow 2FeCl_3$$

a How many atoms of iron are shown on the reactant side of the equation?
b How many molecules of chlorine are shown on the left of the equation?
c How many atoms of chlorine are shown on the left of the equation?
d How many formulas of product are made?
e How many atoms of each element are in one formula of the product?

H 8 Copy and balance the equations. Then add state symbols to show the states at room temperature and pressure.
a $K + H_2O \longrightarrow KOH + H_2$
b $Na + Cl_2 \longrightarrow NaCl$
c $Li + H_2O \longrightarrow LiOH + H_2$
d $Cl_2 + K \longrightarrow KCl$
e $Fe + Cl_2 \longrightarrow FeCl_3$

9 Use the information in the table to work out the formulae of the compounds below.

Positive ions	Negative ions
Na^+	Cl^-
K^+	Br^-
Mg^{2+}	O^{2-}
Ca^{2+}	S^{2-}

a sodium bromide
b potassium chloride
c magnesium sulfide
d potassium oxide

10 Use the information in the table from question 9 to help you answer the questions below.
a The formula of strontium oxide is SrO. What is the formula of the strontium ion?
b The formula of beryllium chloride is $BeCl_2$. What is the formula of the beryllium ion?

1 This question is about strontium and calcium.

Strontium and calcium are in group 2 of the periodic table.

a Strontium is present in foods such as cabbage and onions. Use the periodic table to suggest why, in the body, strontium is absorbed in a similar way to calcium.

_____

_____ [2]

b **i** A calcium atom has 20 electrons. Finish writing its electronic structure below.

2.8. _____ [1]

ii Predict the number of electrons in the outer shell of a strontium atom.

_____ [1]

c The table shows the properties of some group 2 elements. Of the elements shown, calcium is nearest the top of the group, and barium is nearest the bottom of the group.

i Predict the melting point of strontium.

_____ °C [1]

ii Select data from the table to describe the trend in reactivity of the group 2 elements, as you go down the group.

_____

_____ [1]

d Strontium reacts with water to make strontium hydroxide and hydrogen gas.

Write a word equation for the reaction of strontium with water.

_____ [2]

e Use the balanced symbol equation for the reaction of strontium with water to answer the questions below.

$$Sr + 2H_2O \longrightarrow Sr(OH)_2 + H_2$$

i How many atoms of strontium are shown on the left of the equation?

_____ [1]

ii How many molecules of water are shown on the left of the equation?

_____ [1]

iii Give the total number of hydrogen atoms shown in the product side of the equation.

_____ [2]

Total [12]

> **Exam tip**
>
> If the question asks you to select data, you don't need to use all the data. Just refer to the data that helps you to answer the question.

C 4

Name of element	Melting point (°C)	Reaction with water
calcium	850	reacts quite fast with cold water to make calcium hydroxide and hydrogen gas
strontium		reacts very fast with cold water to make strontium hydroxide and hydrogen gas
barium	714	reacts very, very fast with cold water to make barium hydroxide and hydrogen gas

2 Ben uses a science data book to find out the melting points of the hydroxides of some group 1 metals.

He plots the melting points on a bar chart.

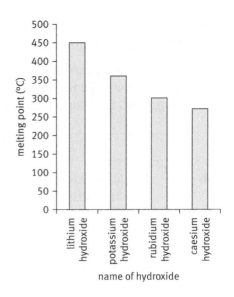

a Describe the trend shown by the bar chart.

_____ [1]

b Ben looks up data about the size of group 1 metal ions.

He writes the data in a table.

Group 1 metal ion	Size (radius) of ion (nm)
lithium ion	0.074
sodium ion	0.102
potassium ion	0.138
rubidium ion	0.149
caesium ion	0.170

Ben develops the explanation below to account for the data in the bar chart.

As the sizes of group 1 metal ions increase, the melting points of their hydroxide compounds decrease.

Ben predicts that the melting point of sodium hydroxide is between 360 °C and 450 °C.

He looks up its melting point in a data book. Its melting point is 319 °C.

Which statement below is correct? Put a tick (✓) in the **one** correct box.

Statement	Tick (✓)
The prediction is incorrect. This proves that the explanation is wrong.	
The prediction is incorrect. This decreases confidence in the explanation.	
The prediction is correct. This increases confidence in the explanation.	
The prediction is correct. This proves that the explanation is correct.	

_____ [1]

c Ben looks up some more data. He writes them in the tables below.

He develops the explanation below.

As the sizes of group 1 and group 2 metal ions increase, the melting points of their chloride compounds decrease.

Name of ion of group 1 metal	Size (radius) of ion (nm)	Melting point of chloride (°C)
lithium	0.074	605
sodium	0.102	801
potassium	0.138	770
rubidium	0.149	718
caesium	0.170	645

Name of ion of group 2 metal	Size (radius) of ion (nm)	melting point of chloride (°C)
beryllium	0.027	405
magnesium	0.072	714
calcium	0.100	782
strontium	0.113	875
barium	0.136	963

Evaluate how well the data in the tables support Ben's explanation.

The quality of written communication will be assessed in your answer to this question.

Write your answer on separate paper or in your exercise book.

Total [8]

3 This question is about sodium fluoride.

a **i** Sodium fluoride consists of sodium and fluoride ions.

The following table shows information about sodium and fluorine atoms and ions.

Complete the table by filling in the empty boxes.

	Number of protons in atom and ion	Number of electrons in atom	Number of electrons in ion	Formula of ion
Sodium	11		10	
Fluorine / fluoride		9		F⁻

[2]

ii Complete the diagram below to show the arrangement of electrons in an ion of sodium. [2]

b Describe what happens to the ions when sodium fluoride dissolves in water.

_____

_____ [1]

c   A solution of sodium fluoride in pure water conducts electricity.

Use ideas about ions to explain why the solution can conduct electricity.

_____

_____ [2]

Total [7]

4 An atom of an element has the electronic structure below:
2.8.8.1

a   i   Calculate the number of electrons in an atom of the element.

_____ [1]

ii   Give the number of protons in an atom of the element.

_____ [1]

b   Use your answers to part a and the periodic table to give the name of the element that has the electronic structure 2.8.8.1.

_____ [1]

Total [3]

Going for the highest grades

5 In solution, chlorine solution displaces bromine from sodium bromide solution.

a   Use the periodic table to help you work out the formula of sodium bromide. Write its formula below.

_____ [1]

b   Write a balanced symbol equation, including state symbols, for the displacement reaction of chlorine with sodium bromide solution.

_____ [3]

Total [4]

Exam tip

Never change the formulae to balance an equation.

1 David and Ruth are pushing on each other's hands. Neither person is moving.

Write **T** next the statements that are true.

Write **F** next to the statements that are false.

a   The size of the force acting on David is less than the size of the force acting on Ruth. ☐

b   The size of the force exerted by David is the same as the size of the force acting on Ruth. ☐

c   Ruth experiences a bigger force than David. ☐

d   Ruth and David exert forces of the same size. ☐

e   The force exerted by Ruth is in the same direction as the force exerted by David. ☐

f   The forces exerted by David and Ruth are opposite in direction. ☐

P 4

2 Draw and label arrows to show the resultant forces on the rope, tricycle, and shopping trolley.

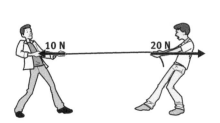

3 Faisal is moving a big loudspeaker.

Which caption belongs where? Write **A**, **B**, or **C** in each box.

A   The friction force has reached its maximum.

B   The size of the friction force is less than its maximum.

C   There is no friction between the loudspeaker and the floor.

I'm pushing really hard, but it's still not moving!

At last! I've got it moving!

4   Kelly goes shopping at the mall. On the right is a distance–time graph for part of her time there.

Label the graph by writing one letter in each box.

A   standing still to look at shoes in a shop window

B   walking quickly from the bus stop to the shops

C   walking slowly past some clothes shops

D   running at a constant speed

Ⓗ E   starting to run when she realises she is late to meet her friend

F   slowing down when she sees her friend in the distance

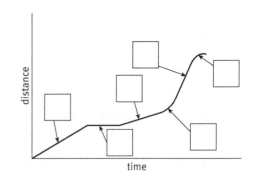

5   Solve the clues to fill in the grid.

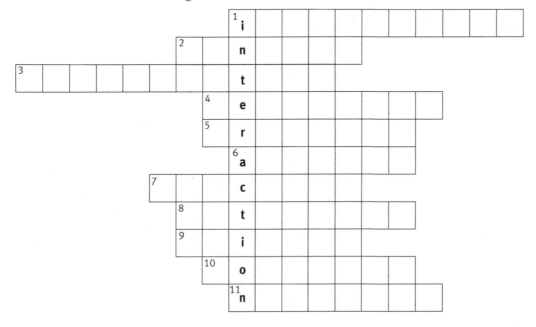

1   The two forces of an _____ pair are equal in size and opposite in direction.

2   A moving object has _____ energy.

3   The change in speed of an object in a given time interval is the _____ of the object.

4   Two people pull on a rope in opposite directions. The sum of the forces on the rope, taking direction into account, is the _____ force.

5   The force of _____ arises when you start pushing something over a surface.

6   Calculate the _____ speed of a car by dividing the total distance by the journey time.

7   A floor exerts a _____ force on a table leg that pushes down on it.

8   If you throw a basketball upwards, its gravitational _____ energy increases.

9   The force that makes you move forwards on a scooter is the _____ force.

10 Multiplying the mass of a train by its velocity gives you the train's _____.

Ⓗ 11 If a football travels in a straight line in one direction, its velocity is positive. When it moves in the opposite direction, its velocity is _____.

What are forces?

P4.2.1–4 Interaction pairs

Lucy and Luke push against each other. They are not moving. Lucy exerts a force on Luke. Luke exerts a force on Lucy.

- Forces arise from an **interaction** between two objects. They come in pairs.
- Each force in an **interaction pair** acts on a different object. The forces are **equal** in size and **opposite** in direction.

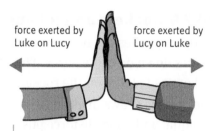

force exerted by Luke on Lucy · force exerted by Lucy on Luke

The arrows show the sizes and directions of the forces.

P4.3.1–2 Resultant force

The **resultant force** on an object is the sum of the individual forces that act on it, taking their directions into account.

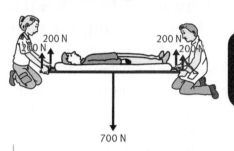

The resultant force on the stretcher is 100 N in an upward direction. The stretcher starts moving up from the ground.

P4.2.6 Reaction of surfaces

Vincent's feet push down on the floor. The floor pushes up on his feet with an equal force. This force is the **reaction of the surface**.

P4.2.5, P4.2.7 Friction

David tries to push a skip. The force of **friction** stops the skip sliding over the road's surface.

As David pushes harder, the size of the friction force increases. Eventually, the friction force reaches its limit. Now the skip moves.

There was no friction force between the skip and the road before David tried to push the skip. Friction arose in response to the force that David applied.

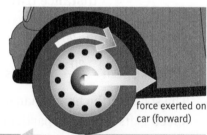

friction at its maximum (less than 6000 N)

The skip moves. 6000 N is bigger than the maximum possible friction force for this skip and the road surface.

friction = 2500 N

The friction force balances David's push. The skip does not move.

friction = 5000 N

The friction force balances David's push. The skip still does not move.

How do objects start moving?

P4.2.8 Using friction

When a car engine starts, the wheels turn. They exert a backward-pushing force on the road surface. The other force in the interaction pair, the forward force, is the same size. This gets the car moving.

When you walk, your foot pushes back on the ground. The friction between your foot and the ground pushes you forward with an equal force.

force exerted on car (forward)

force exerted by tyre on road (backwards)

The tyre grips the road. The road exerts a large forward force on the axle. This pushes the car forward.

P4.2.9 Rockets and jet engines

A rocket pushes out hot gases as its fuel burns. The rocket pushes down on these gases. The escaping gases exert an equal and opposite force on the rocket, and push the rocket upwards.

A jet engine draws in air at the front and pushes it out at the back. An equal and opposite force pushes the engine forwards.

Why do objects keep moving?
P4.3.6–7 Driving and counter forces

Alex pushes Sam along on a skateboard. Alex exerts the **driving force** to push it forward. There is a **counter force** in the opposite direction, because of air resistance and friction.

- If the driving force is greater than the counter force, the skateboard speeds up.
- If the driving force is equal to the counter force, the skateboard moves at a constant speed in a straight line.
- If the driving force is less than the counter force, the skateboard slows down.

force exerted upwards on the rocket

force exerted downwards on the hot gases

driving force

counter force

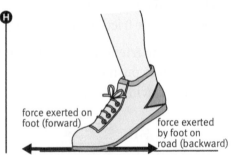

H

force exerted on foot (forward)

force exerted by foot on road (backward)

P4.1.1–2, P4.1.9 Speed and velocity

You can use the equation below to calculate **average speed**.

$$\text{speed (m/s)} = \frac{\text{distance travelled (m)}}{\text{time (s)}}$$

So if a horse runs 20 metres in 10 seconds:

$$\text{average speed} = \frac{20 \text{ m}}{10 \text{ s}} = 2 \text{ m/s}$$

The speed of the horse changes as it runs. Its **instantaneous speed** is its speed at a particular instant, or its average speed over a very short time interval.

The **instantaneous velocity** of an object is its instantaneous speed in a certain direction.

P4.1.8, P4.1.13 Acceleration

If a car gets faster, it is accelerating. The **acceleration** of the car is its change of speed, or change of velocity, in a given time interval. You can use the equation here to calculate acceleration:

$$\text{acceleration (m/s)} = \frac{\text{change in velocity (m/s)}}{\text{time taken (s)}}$$

If a car accelerates from 10 m/s to 30 m/s in 10 s:

$$\text{acceleration} = \frac{(30 - 10)\ \text{m/s}}{10\ \text{s}}$$
$$= 2\ \text{m/s}^2$$

P 4

How can we describe motion?
4.1.3–6 Distance–time and displacement–time graphs

Distance–time graphs describe movement.

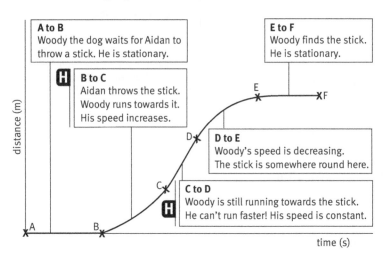

A to B
Woody the dog waits for Aidan to throw a stick. He is stationary.

E to F
Woody finds the stick. He is stationary.

H **B to C**
Aidan throws the stick. Woody runs towards it. His speed increases.

D to E
Woody's speed is decreasing. The stick is somewhere round here.

C to D
Woody is still running towards the stick. He can't run faster! His speed is constant. **H**

H You can use distance–time graphs to calculate speed.

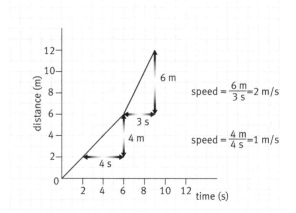

$$\text{speed} = \frac{6\ \text{m}}{3\ \text{s}} = 2\ \text{m/s}$$

$$\text{speed} = \frac{4\ \text{m}}{4\ \text{s}} = 1\ \text{m/s}$$

The steeper the gradient of a distance–time graph, the greater the speed.

H The **displacement** of an object at a given moment is the straight-line distance from its starting point, with an indication of direction. Freya throws a ball into the air. The graphs show how its distance and displacement change with time.

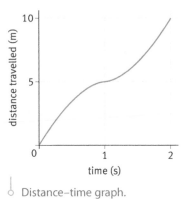

Distance–time graph.

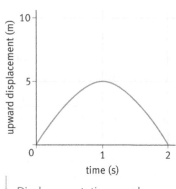

Displacement–time graph.

P4.1.7, P4.1.10–12 Speed–time and velocity–time graphs

Speed–time graphs show how speed varies with time. The graph opposite shows the speed of a train on a 3-hour journey.

Ⓗ Velocity–time graphs show the velocity of an object at every instant of its journey. The graph below shows the velocity of Ella, an ice dancer. The gradient of a section of the graph is equal to Ella's acceleration.

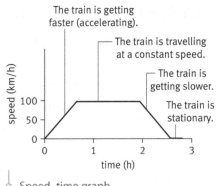

The train is getting faster (accelerating).

The train is travelling at a constant speed.

The train is getting slower.

The train is stationary.

Speed–time graph.

How are forces and motion connected?
P4.3.3–5, P4.3.11 Momentum

All moving objects have **momentum**.

momentum (kg m/s) = **mass** (kg) × **velocity** (m/s)

For a 0.5 kg bird flying at a velocity of 2 m/s:

momentum = 0.5 kg × 2 m/s
= 1 kg m/s

When a resultant force acts on an object, the momentum of the object changes in the direction of the force:

change of momentum = resultant force × time for which it acts
(kg m/s)   (newton, N)   (second, s)

If a 3-second gust of wind from behind a bird exerts a resultant force of 10 N on the bird:

change of momentum = 10 N × 3 s
= 30 kg m/s in the direction the bird is flying

If the resultant force on an object is zero, its momentum does not change:
- If it is stationary, it stays still.
- If it is already moving, it continues at a steady speed in a straight line.

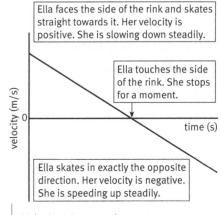

Ⓗ

Ella faces the side of the rink and skates straight towards it. Her velocity is positive. She is slowing down steadily.

Ella touches the side of the rink. She stops for a moment.

Ella skates in exactly the opposite direction. Her velocity is negative. She is speeding up steadily.

Velocity–time graph.

P4.3.8–9 Road safety

If two cars collide and stop, their momentum changes until it becomes zero. The more time the change of momentum takes, the smaller the resultant force. Road safety measures use this idea:
- Car **crumple zones** squash slowly in a collision. So the collision lasts longer, and the resultant force on the car is less.
- **Seat belts** stretch in a collision. This makes the change of momentum take longer. So the force is less.
- **Helmets** change shape when they hit something. Your head stops moving more slowly, so the force on it is less.
- **Air bags** also increase the time for the change of momentum.

How can we use energy changes to describe motion?
P4.4.1, P4.4.3–5, P4.4.8–13 Doing work

Barney takes his child to the park. He pushes the buggy with a force of 15 N. The force makes the buggy move. Barney is **doing work**.

work done by a force = force × distance moved by the force
     (joule, J)   (newton, N)   (metre, m)

The park is 500 m away from Barney's house. So:
work done by Barney = 15 N × 500 m = 7500 J

Barney **transfers energy** to the buggy. His store of chemical energy decreases. The energy of the buggy increases.

amount of energy transferred = work done
         (joule, J)   (joule, J)

amount of energy transferred by Barney = work done = 7500 J

The moving buggy has **kinetic energy (KE)**. Kinetic energy depends on **mass** and **velocity**.

kinetic energy = ½ ×   mass   ×   (velocity)^2
    (joule, J)   (kilogram, kg)   (metre per second, m/s)^2

So the faster the buggy moves, and the greater the mass of the child in it, the more kinetic energy it has.

If Barney pushes with a greater force, he does more work and so transfers more energy. The buggy goes faster and its kinetic energy increases.

In fact, the gain of kinetic energy by the buggy is less than the energy transferred from Barney. Barney must also transfer enough energy to overcome air resistance and friction. This energy is transferred to the surroundings as heat.

Overall, as in every event and process, energy is conserved.

P4.3.10, P4.4.2,6,7,14 Gravitational potential energy

Catherine picks up her doll from the ground. She is doing work. The doll's **gravitational potential energy (GPE)** increases.

change in GPE =   weight   × vertical height difference
   (joule, J)   (newton, N)   (metre, m)

The doll's weight is 3 N. Catherine lifts it 1 m. So:

change in doll's GPE = 3 N × 1 m = 3 J

Catherine lets go of the doll. The force of gravity pulls it downwards. The doll falls 1 m to the ground. Its kinetic energy increases and its GPE decreases.

GPE lost = kinetic energy gained

So the doll gains 3 J of kinetic energy.

ⓗ To calculate the doll's speed as it falls:

KE = ½ × mass × (velocity)^2

The doll's mass is 0.3 kg.
Rearranging gives:

$$velocity = \sqrt{\frac{2 \times \text{kinetic energy}}{\text{mass}}}$$

$$= \sqrt{\frac{(2 \times 3 \text{ J})}{0.3 \text{ kg}}}$$

$$= \sqrt{(20 \text{ J/kg}}$$

$$= 4.5 \text{ m/s}$$

1   Use the words in the box to fill in the gaps. Each word may be used once, more than once, or not at all.

average	constant	increasing	gravity
friction	instantaneous	short	long
upwards	downwards	decreasing	time

A bird of prey flies from one tree to another in a straight line. Its _____ speed is equal to the distance between the trees, divided by its flying _____. Its instantaneous speed is its average speed over a very _____ time interval.

The bird drops to the ground. The force of _____ pulls the bird downwards. Air resistance exerts an _____ force on the bird.

The bird takes off again and flies along at a steady speed in a straight line. While it flies along, its momentum is _____.

2   Saima pulls along her suitcase.
The arrows show the directions of the counter force and the driving force.

driving force
counter-force

Write **T** next to the statements that are true.
Write **F** next to the statements that are false.
a   If the driving force is less than the counter force, the suitcase slows down.
b   Saima exerts a driving force to pull along the suitcase.
c   If the driving force is equal to the counter force, the suitcase moves with a constant speed.
d   The counter force is caused by air resistance only.
e   If the driving force is more than the counter force, the suitcase speeds up.
f   The counter force is caused by air resistance and friction.
g   If the driving force is equal to the counter force, the suitcase cannot move.

3   Highlight the correct word in each pair of **bold** words.
a   The faster an object moves, the **smaller / greater** its kinetic energy.
b   Ali lifts a weight. Energy is transferred from **the weight / Ali** to **the weight /Ali**.
c   Harry pulls a toy sledge across the carpet. Friction causes the sledge to gain **less / more** kinetic energy than the work Harry put in to pulling the sledge, because some energy is dissipated through **heating / pulling**.

4   Calculate the average speed of the following. Include units in your answers.
a   a helicopter that travels 600 metres in 3 minutes
b   a football that travels 80 metres in 2 seconds
c   a racehorse that runs 900 metres in 50 seconds
d   a worm that moves 32 centimetres in 8 seconds
5   Calculate the acceleration of the following. Include units in your answers.
a   a runner whose velocity increases from 0 m/s to 10 m/s in 2 seconds
b   a car whose velocity increases from 10 m/s to 30 m/s in 10 seconds
6   Calculate the momentum of each of the following:
a   a 2000 kg sports car moving at a velocity of 44 m/s
b   a 70 kg person on a 6 kg scooter moving at a velocity of 4 m/s
c   a 9 kg baby crawling at a velocity of 1.5 m/s
7   A driver does an emergency stop as a child runs out in front of her car. The car stops in 3 seconds. The resultant force on the car is 5000 N. Calculate the change in momentum.
8   Calculate the kinetic energy of each of the following:
a   a 150 kg lion running with a velocity of 20 m/s
b   a 4000 kg bus moving with a velocity of 25 m/s
c   a 60 g tennis ball moving with a velocity of 44 m/s
9   Use the idea of a pair of equal and opposite forces to explain how jet engines produce a driving force.
H 10   Pawel is a swimmer.
Here is his velocity–time graph for the first 55 m of a 100-m race.

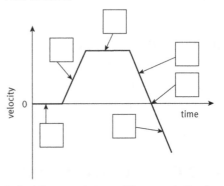

Label the graph by writing one letter in each box.
A   Pawel is waiting to dive in. He is stationary.
B   Pawel is moving in a straight line. His speed is steadily increasing.
C   Pawel has turned round. He has changed direction. His speed is steadily increasing.
D   Pawel is moving in a straight line. He is swimming at a constant speed.
E   Pawel is turning round. He is stationary for an instant.
F   Pawel is moving in a straight line. He is slowing down.

1   A penguin stands at the top of a slope. It slides to the bottom.

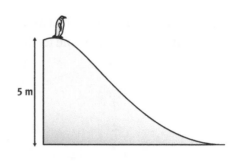

5 m

   a   i   As the penguin slides down the slope its gravitational
        potential energy (GPE) and its kinetic energy (KE)
        change.

        Tick the statements that are true.

        The GPE of the penguin at the top of the
        slope is less than its GPE at the bottom.   ☐

        As the penguin slides down the slope, its
        GPE decreases.   ☐

        The force of gravity does work on the
        penguin as it slides down the slope.   ☐

        The penguin's velocity increases as it
        slides down the slope.   ☐

        As the penguin slides down the slope, it
        gains KE.   ☐   [2]

   ii   Calculate the change in the penguin's gravitational
        potential energy.

        The weight of the penguin is 300 N.

        Change in GPE = _____ J   [2]

   iii   Assume that friction is small enough to ignore.

        What is the change in the penguin's kinetic energy?

        Change in KE = _____ J   [1]

   b   A baby penguin travels down the same slope.

        Its mass is 6 kg.

        Its velocity at the bottom of the slope is 10 m/s.

        Calculate the kinetic energy of the baby penguin at the
        bottom of the slope.

        KE = _____ J   [2]

        Total [7]

> **Exam tip**
>
> Don't forget to show your
> working in calculations. If
> your answer is wrong, but
> your working is correct, you
> might still get a mark.

2   Look at the pictures of the lorries.

   Lorry A and lorry B have the same mass and their tyres are
   the same.

   The shape of lorry A means that it experiences less air
   resistance than lorry B.

   Use ideas about forces in interaction pairs to explain why the
   driving force needed by lorry B is less than the driving force
   needed by lorry A, when they travel in a straight line at a
   steady speed.

**P
4**

Assume the loads on the two lorries, and the weather and road conditions, are the same for both lorries.

A   B

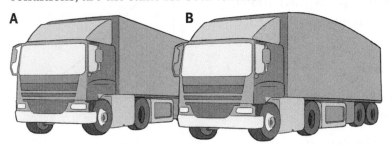

✎ The quality of written communication will be assessed in your answer to this question.

Write your answer on separate paper or in your exercise book.

Total [6]

3 A fire engine travels to a fire.

The graph shows its journey.

a **i** In which part of the journey was the fire engine moving along most slowly?

Draw a (ring) around the correct answer.

A to B   B to C   C to D   D to E   E to F [1]

ii Describe the motion of the fire engine from **B to D**.

_____

_____ [2]

iii Calculate the average speed of the fire engine between **A and B**.

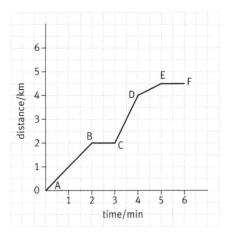

Average speed = _____ km/minute   [2]

b A police car travels to the same fire. It goes 6000 metres in 500 seconds.

Calculate the average speed of the police car.

Average speed = _____ m/s   [2]

Total [7]

4 Oona used a book to find the fastest speeds of some animals. She wrote the speeds in a table.

Animal	Fastest speed (m/s)
cheetah	28
horse	17
cat	13
elephant	11
pig	6
chicken	4
mouse	3
snail	0.01

Opposite are distance–time and speed–time graphs for some of the animals in the table.

On the graphs, the animals in the table above are represented by letters.

a On the **speed–time graph**, animal E is a chicken and animal H is a cheetah.

What might be the identities of animals F and G?

Put a tick (✓) in the box next to the **one** correct statement.

F = snail	G = chicken	☐
F = cat	G = horse	☐
F = cat	G = chicken	☐
F = chicken	G = snail	☐ [1]

b Use the **distance–time graph** to calculate the top speeds of animals A and B.

_____

_____ [2]

c Which of the following are correct conclusions from the distance–time graph?

Put ticks (✓) in the boxes next to the **two** correct statements.

The top speed of animal B is twice the top speed of animal A. ☐

There is no animal in the world that has a slower top speed than animal A. ☐

The top speed of animal D is 11 m/s. ☐

Animal C is unlikely to be a pig. ☐

The graph shows that animal D is the fastest animal in the world. ☐ [2]

Total [5]

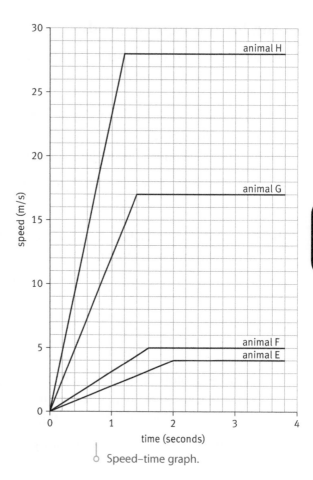

Speed–time graph.

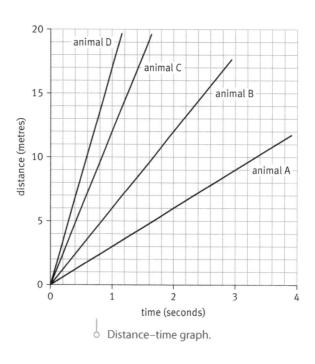

Distance–time graph.

Going for the highest grades

H **5** A motorbike goes along a straight test track.

- For the first 6 seconds it accelerates until it reaches a speed of 40 m/s.
- For the next 4 seconds it moves at a steady speed.
- Then it slows down.
- It stops 14 seconds after its journey began.

a Finish the velocity–time graph for the journey:

[3]

b Calculate the acceleration of the motorbike during the first 6 seconds of its journey.

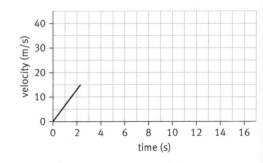

Answer = _____ m/s² [2]

c Another motorbike travels along the same straight test track at a speed of 30 m/s. It then turns round and goes back along the same test track at the same speed.

Describe the change in velocity of the motorbike.

_____

_____ [1]

d A third motorbike travels along the test track.

The graph opposite shows how the displacement of the bike changes with time.

i What is the displacement of the bike at 10 seconds? Include the unit in your answer.

_____ [1]

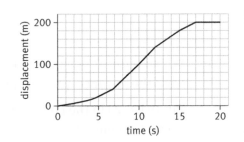

ii Describe the motion of the motorbike between 12 and 15 seconds.

_____

_____ [2]

Total [9]

1   The flow diagram is about mitosis and meiosis in humans.

Use words and numbers from the box to fill in the gaps.
Use each word or number once, more than once, or not at all.
The pictures in the flow diagram may help you.

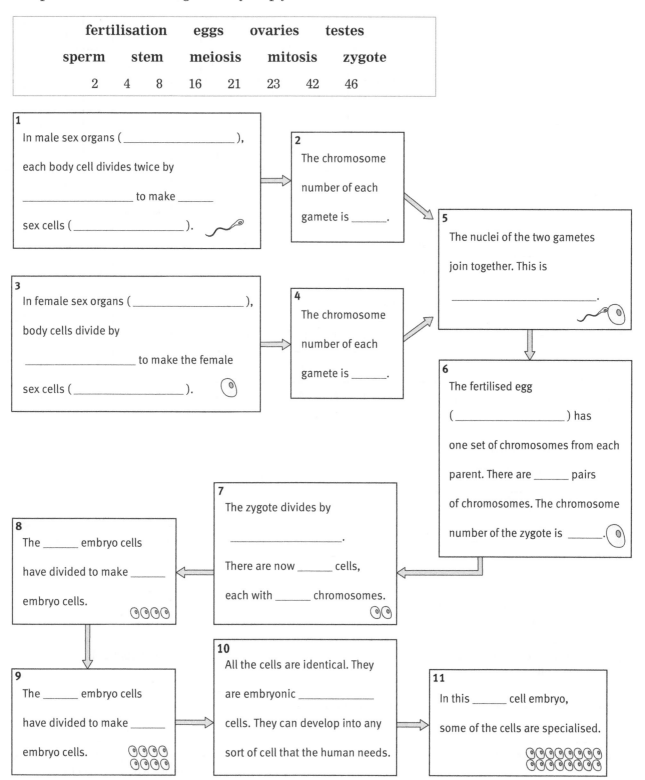

fertilisation	eggs	ovaries	testes
sperm	stem	meiosis	mitosis	zygote
2	4	8	16	21	23	42	46

1
In male sex organs (_____),

each body cell divides twice by

_____ to make _____

sex cells (_____).

2
The chromosome

number of each

gamete is _____.

5
The nuclei of the two gametes

join together. This is

_____.

3
In female sex organs (_____),

body cells divide by

_____ to make the female

sex cells (_____).

4
The chromosome

number of each

gamete is _____.

6
The fertilised egg

(_____) has

one set of chromosomes from each

parent. There are _____ pairs

of chromosomes. The chromosome

number of the zygote is _____.

7
The zygote divides by

_____.

There are now _____ cells,

each with _____ chromosomes.

8
The _____ embryo cells

have divided to make _____

embryo cells.

9
The _____ embryo cells

have divided to make _____

embryo cells.

10
All the cells are identical. They

are embryonic _____

cells. They can develop into any

sort of cell that the human needs.

11
In this _____ cell embryo,

some of the cells are specialised.

B5

2 All the words in this wordsearch are about the growth and development of plants and animals.

   Find one word beginning with each of the letters in the table.
   Write a crossword-type clue for each word.

Word	Clue
A	
C	
E	
F	
G	
M	
N	
O	
P	
T	
U	
X	
Y	
Z	

H	C	D	E	M	O	S	O	B	I	R	T	A	S	C
P	H	O	T	O	T	R	O	P	I	S	M	R	U	E
T	R	U	N	S	P	E	C	I	A	L	I	S	E	D
I	O	B	A	S	E	S	S	E	U	N	T	T	L	I
S	M	L	H	A	M	E	L	Y	X	R	O	E	C	A
S	O	E	G	P	P	I	L	I	I	H	C	M	U	P
U	S	H	A	E	N	R	A	G	N	B	H	C	N	A
E	O	E	M	B	R	Y	O	N	I	C	O	E	M	Y
G	M	L	E	E	F	E	T	U	S	Y	N	L	R	A
H	E	I	T	T	A	K	D	O	R	A	D	L	W	D
T	N	X	E	E	T	O	G	Y	Z	E	R	S	E	L
J	Y	A	S	S	E	I	N	A	C	T	I	V	E	O
X	S	E	M	M	S	E	L	L	E	N	A	G	R	O

3 Fill in the empty boxes to show the differences between mitosis and meiosis.

	Meiosis	Mitosis
What does it make?	gametes (sex cells)	
How many new cells does each parent cell make?		2
How many chromosomes are in each new cell?		same as in parent cell
Where does it happen?	in sex organs	
Why does it happen?		so an organism can grow, reproduce and replace damaged cells

B5.1.1–2 What's inside a plant or animal?

Animals and plants are **multicellular organisms**. They are made up of many cells. The cells can be **specialised** to do certain jobs.

In animals and plants, specialised cells of the same type are grouped together to form **tissues**, for example, muscle tissue. Groups of tissues form **organs**, for example, the heart.

B5.1.3–6 What are human stem cells?

Humans develop from a single fertilised egg, or **zygote**. The zygote divides to form new cells. This ball of cells is an **embryo**. When the embryo consists of eight cells or fewer, all its cells are identical. These are **embryonic stem cells**. Each one could produce any type of cell that the growing human needs.

After the eight-cell stage, most embryo cells become specialised. They form different types of tissue. By about eight weeks, these tissues have grouped together to form the main organs. The growing human is now a **fetus**.

Some cells remain unspecialised until adulthood. These are **adult stem cells**. They can develop into many types of specialised cells.

B5.1.7–9 How do plants grow?

Most plant cells are specialised. Specialised plant cells are grouped together to form tissues such as:
- xylem, which transports water through the plant's organs
- phloem, which transports sugar.

Groups of tissues are organised into organs, for example, leaves, flowers, stems, and roots.

Plant cells at root tips and shoot tips remain unspecialised. So do rings of cells in stems and roots. These are **meristem cells**. They divide to make new cells that can develop into any type of cell.

Meristem cells explain why plants can grow throughout their lives, and why plants can regrow whole new organs if they are damaged.

B5.1.10–11 What are cuttings?

Gardeners sometimes grow plants from **cuttings**. The new plant and the parent plant are genetically identical. They are **clones**.

First, the gardener chooses a plant with features that he wants. He cuts a piece of stem from the plant. This is a cutting. The gardener dips the cut end in **rooting powder**. Rooting powder contains plant hormones, or **auxins**.

The meristem cells in the cuttings divide to make new cells. Plant hormones encourage some of these cells to develop into root cells. Other unspecialised cells become tissues that form other organs.

B5.1.12–14 How does light affect plant growth?

Plants tend to grow towards the light. This is **phototropism**. Plants need light to photosynthesise. So phototropism increases a plant's chance of survival.

 Phototropism involves **auxins**.

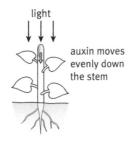
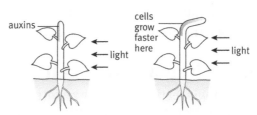

If light is above a growing shoot, auxins spread out evenly.
The shoot grows straight up.

auxin moves evenly down the stem

If light comes from the side, auxins move to the shady side. Auxins make cells on the shady side grow faster. So the shoot bends towards the light.

B5.2.1–2 How does mitosis make new body cells?

First, a cell grows. During growth, it makes copies of:
• its **organelles** (specialised parts) including mitochondria
• its chromosomes – these are copied when the two strands of each DNA molecule separate and new strands form alongside them.

Next, **mitosis** happens. In mitosis the chromosome copies separate and go to opposite ends of the cell. Then the whole cell (including the nucleus) divides to make two new cells. The new cells are genetically identical to each other and to the parent cell.

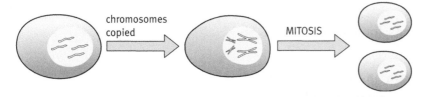

chromosomes copied

MITOSIS

Mitosis of a cell with 4 chromosomes.

B5.2.3–4 How does meiosis make new sex cells?

Meiosis makes sex cells (**gametes**). It happens in sex organs.
In meiosis, a body cell divides twice. The resulting cells may develop into gametes. Gametes are not identical – they each carry different genetic information.

Gametes have half the number of chromosomes as the parent cell.
Human body cells have 46 chromosomes, arranged in 23 pairs.
So human gametes (sperm and egg cells) have only 23 single chromosomes.

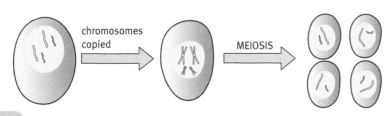

chromosomes copied

MEIOSIS

Meiosis of a cell with 4 chromosomes.

Fertilisation

When a human sperm cell fertilises an egg cell, their nuclei join up. The fertilised egg cell (**zygote**) gets one set of chromosomes from each parent. It has 23 chromosome pairs – 46 chromosomes in all.

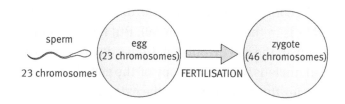

B5.3.1–4 What's in DNA?

The nucleus of each of your body cells contains enough information to determine the characteristics of your whole body. This information is the **genetic code**.

The genetic code is stored in chromosomes. A chromosome is a very long molecule of **DNA** wound around a protein framework. A human DNA molecule is made up of about 30 000 genes.

A DNA molecule contains two strands twisted together in a spiral. This is a **double helix**.

- Each strand is made of four bases: adenine (A), thymine (T), guanine (G), and cytosine (C).
- The bases on the two strands of a DNA molecule always pair up in the same way – A pairs with T, and G pairs with C. This is **base pairing**.

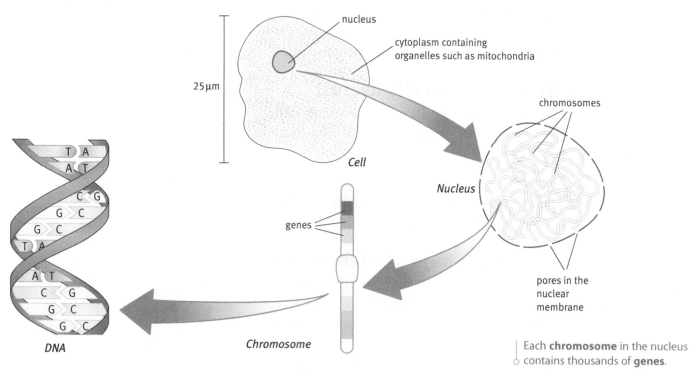

Each **chromosome** in the nucleus contains thousands of **genes**.

Cells make proteins. There are thousands of different proteins. The order of the bases in a gene is the genetic code for making a particular protein.

Ⓗ Cells make proteins by joining together **amino acids**. Each protein has a certain combination of amino acids joined together in a particular order. The order of bases in a gene is the code for building up amino acids in the correct order to make a particular protein.

B5.3.5–6 Where do cells make proteins?

DNA contains the genetic code for making proteins. DNA is in the nucleus of a cell. But new proteins are made in the cell cytoplasm. Genes do not leave the cell nucleus. Instead, a copy of the gene is made. This carries the genetic code to the cytoplasm.

H The copy of the gene that carries the code is called **messenger RNA**.

B5.3.7–8 Why are some genes switched off?

The nucleus of each of your body cells contains an exact copy of the DNA of the original zygote. So every cell contains the same genes. But not all these genes are active in every cell. Each cell makes only the proteins it needs to be a particular type of cell. Genes that give instructions to make other proteins are not active; they are **switched off**.

For example, hair cells make keratin. In hair cells, the genes for the enzymes that make keratin are switched on. Hair cells do not make muscle. So the genes for the enzymes that make muscle are switched off.

Salivary gland cells make amylase. In these cells, the genes for the enzymes that make amylase are switched on. The genes for the enzymes that make keratin and muscle are switched off.

B5.3.9–10 How are stem cells useful?

Scientists are doing a lot of research on stem cells. Adult stem cells, and embryonic stem cells, may make specialised cells to:

*   replace damaged tissue
*   treat some diseases.

There are ethical issues to consider when using embryonic stem cells, so there are government regulations to control this research.

B5.3.11 How do clones form specialised cells?

H Scientists have made clones of animals such as sheep, and of tissues and organs of other mammals, including humans. The process involves reactivating, or switching on, inactive genes in adult body cell nuclei.

This is how to produce an organ or tissue needed by a patient:

*   Take a nucleus out of a human egg cell. Replace it with a nucleus from a body cell of the patient.
*   The egg cell divides by mitosis and makes an embryo. The genes in the embryo are the same as the patient's genes.
*   After 5 days, put stem cells from the embryo in a dish of nutrients.
*   The stem cells can develop into different types of tissue or organ.
*   Transplant the organ or tissue required into the patient.

unspecialised cell

None of the genes are switched off on in this chromosome.

hair cell

salivary gland cell

Different genes are switched off in specialised cells.

Key

⬜ gene switched on   ⬜ gene switched off

Some proteins are found in each type of cell, for example, the enzymes needed for respiration. All cells respire, so the genes needed for respiration are switched on in all cells.

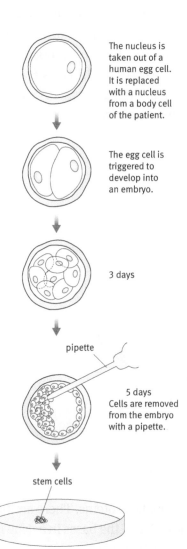

The nucleus is taken out of a human egg cell. It is replaced with a nucleus from a body cell of the patient.

The egg cell is triggered to develop into an embryo.

3 days

pipette

5 days
Cells are removed from the embryo with a pipette.

stem cells

Stem cells from the embryo are grown in a dish containing nutrients.

Stem cells develop into different tissues and organs. These can be used for medical treatment.

Therapeutic cloning.

B 5

Use extra paper to answer these questions if you need to.

1 Write **P** next to the statements that are true for plants only, **A** next to the statements that are true for animals only, and **B** next to the statements that are true for both.
   a Can grow in height and width for their whole lives. __
   b Contain organs. __
   c Grow only at meristems. __
   d Contain groups of similar cells called tissues. __
   e Contain specialised cells. __
   f Can regrow whole organs if they are damaged. __

2 Use words from the box to fill in the gaps. Each word may be used once, more than once, or not at all.

> mitochondria   mitosis   organelles   DNA   cell
>
> strands   meiosis   chromosomes   nucleus

In the cell cycle, cells grow. During cell growth, the numbers of _____ increase, including _____. Also, the _____ are copied. This happens when two strands of each _____ molecule separate and new _____ form alongside them.
Then _____ happens. During this process, copies of the _____ separate and the _____ divides.

3 Fill in the empty boxes.

Species	Number of chromosomes in sex cell	Number of chromosomes in body cell
horse	32	
wolf		78
carp	52	
		46

4 Draw lines to match each base in DNA with the base it pairs up with.

Base
A
T
C
G

Base
A
T
C
G

5 Write **T** next to the statements that are **true**. Write corrected versions of the statements that are **false**.
   a Up to the 16-cell stage, all the cells in a human embryo are identical.

b Embryonic stem cells can produce any type of cell needed by a human.
c Adult stem cells can produce any type of cell needed by a human.
d A zygote divides by meiosis to form an embryo.
e A zygote contains a set of chromosomes from each parent.
f In a 16-cell human embryo, most of the embryo cells are specialised.
g Groups of specialised cells in an animal are called zygotes.
h Cell division by meiosis produces new cells that are genetically identical to the parent cell.
i Cell division by mitosis produces new cells that are genetically identical to each other.
j Meiosis makes gametes.

6 Tick the boxes to show which genes are switched on in the cells below. Hint: nails and hair contain a protein called keratin.

Cell	Are these genes switched on?		
	gene to make keratin	gene to make salivary amylase	gene for respiration
nail			
hair			
embryonic stem cell			
salivary gland cell			
muscle cell			

7 Write down where in a cell the processes below happen.
   a A copy of a gene is made.
   b Proteins are produced.
   c Aerobic respiration.

H 8 Draw arrows to show where the light is coming from for each of the plant shoots below. Shade each plant shoot to show where the concentration of auxins is greatest.

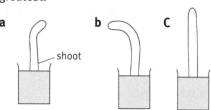

9 Name the chemical that carries the genetic code from the nucleus to the cytoplasm of a cell.
10 Explain how DNA codes for the making of proteins.

1 Giraffes have 30 chromosomes in each body cell.

a Finish the sentences by choosing the best words and numbers from the box.

Use each word or number once, more than once, or not at all.

gametes	zygotes	different	ovaries	testes
penis	identical	1 2 4	15	30 60

Giraffes make sex cells by meiosis. Sex cells are also

called _____. In male giraffes, meiosis

happens in the _____. In meiosis, one body

cell divides to make _____ sex cells. Each of these cells

carries _____ genetic information. There are

_____ chromosomes in one giraffe sex cell. [5]

b After sexual intercourse, the nucleus of a male sex cell joins to the nucleus of a female sex cell.

i Give the name of the female sex cell.

_____ [1]

ii Give the name of the process in which the nucleus of a male sex cell joins to the nucleus of a female sex cell.

_____ [1]

c The steps below describe how body cells grow and divide in giraffe embryos.

They are in the wrong order.

A The chromosome copies separate and go to opposite ends of the cell.

B These are identical to each other and to the parent cell.

C The cell makes copies of its specialised parts, including the chromosomes.

D The cell divides to make two new cells.

Fill in the boxes to show the correct order. [3]

☐ ☐ ☐ ☐ **Total [10]**

2 James has a rose plant.

He cuts a piece of stem from the plant. This is a cutting.

He dips the end of the cutting in rooting powder, and plants it in compost.

The cutting grows roots.

A new rose plant grows.

a **i** Why do gardeners take cuttings?

Tick the **two best** reasons.

They can grow many new plants quickly
and cheaply. ☐

They can grow many new plants with
different features by taking cuttings from
just one plant. ☐

Plants grown from cuttings are more
resistant to disease than plants grown
from seed. ☐

They can reproduce a plant with exactly
the features they want. ☐

Plants grown from cuttings are stronger
than plants grown from seed ☐ [1]

ii Give the name of the plant hormone in
rooting powder.

_____ [1]

b Vijay is investigating cuttings.

He takes 10 stems from a hedge plant.

He removes the leaves from the bottom 5 cm of the stems.

He dips the cut ends in water.

He dips the wet ends of 5 stems in rooting powder.

He plants all 10 stems in compost in plant pots.

After two weeks, he removes the stems from the pots.

He washes the compost off the stems.

He counts the roots that are growing in each stem.

He writes his results in a table.

| | Number of roots after 2 weeks | | | | | |
	Test 1	Test 2	Test 3	Test 4	Test 5	Mean
Cuttings with rooting powder	7	6	9	5	5	
Cuttings without rooting powder	3	4	0	2	0	

i Complete the table by calculating the mean values.
Record the mean values in the empty boxes, rounding
each answer to the nearest whole number. [2]

ii Suggest why Vijay used 5 cuttings with rooting powder, and 5 cuttings without, instead of using just one cutting in each of the two conditions.

_____

_____ [1]

iii Write a conclusion to Vijay's experiment.

_____

_____ [1]

Exam tip

When writing conclusions, make sure you clearly describe any correlations between factors.

c Vijay finds the graph below in a text book. Describe what the graph shows.

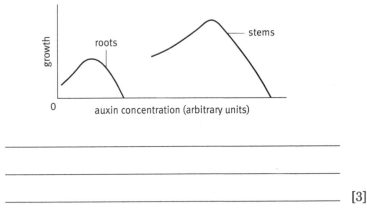

Exam tip

When describing what a graph shows, make sure you describe relationships between the factors of the axes for each part of the graph.

_____

_____

_____ [3]

Total: [9]

3 A company sells 'stem cell gift certificates'.

When a baby is born, a nurse takes blood from the baby's umbilical cord. The company separates stem cells from the blood. It stores the stem cells at −180 °C for 25 years.

a i What are stem cells?

Put a tick next to the **best** definition.

Stem cells are unspecialised cells. They join together to make specialised cells. ☐

Stem cells are unspecialised cells. They divide and develop into specialised cells. ☐

Stem cells are specialised cells. They divide and develop into unspecialised cells. ☐

Stem cells are specialised cells. They join together to make unspecialised cells. ☐ [1]

ii The company says that doctors can use the stem cells to treat illnesses the baby may get in future.

How might doctors use the stem cells to treat heart disease?

Put a tick next to the **most likely** answer.

They will make a heart disease vaccine from the stem cells. ☐

They will grow heart muscle cells from the stem cells. ☐

They will make a heart disease medicine from the stem cells. ☐

They will inject stem cells into the patient's bloodstream. ☐ [1]

B 5

iii Some friends are discussing removing and storing umbilical cord blood.

Here are their ideas.

Ben — *At the moment, stem cells can be used to treat only a few diseases.*

Sylvia — *There is only a small chance that, in future, your son or daughter will get a disease that can be treated by stem cells.*

Adam — *In future, stem cells may be used to treat many diseases.*

Menna — *No one knows how long stem cells can be stored for.*

Simon — *Taking blood from the umbilical cord will distract the midwives when they should be concentrating on making sure mother and baby are safe and well.*

Amanda — *Imagine your son or daughter gets a disease that could be treated by umbilical cord stem cells, and you didn't keep any. How would you feel?*

Write a paragraph to advise a pregnant woman whether she **should** *or* **should not** have her baby's umbilical cord blood stored.

Select reasons from the speech bubbles to support your answer.

_____

_____

_____

_____ [3]

b One source of stem cells is umbilical cord blood.

    i Name **one other** source of stem cells.

    _____ [1]

    ii Give one **problem** of using stem cells from this source to treat disease or replace damaged tissues.

    _____

    _____ [1]

Total: [7]

4 Describe the differences and similarities between mitosis and meiosis.

✎ The quality of written communication will be assessed in your answer to this question.

Write your answer on separate paper or in your exercise book.

Total [6]

Going for the highest grades

Ⓗ 5 Explain why, in a specialised body cell, many genes are inactive (switched off).

Describe the conditions in which inactive genes in a body cell may be reactivated (switched on) to form cells of all tissue types.

✎ The quality of written communication will be assessed in your answer to this question.

Write your answer on separate paper or in your exercise book.

Total [6]

1 Look at the diagram below and complete the boxes like this:

- Write the letters A, B, and C in the correct small squares.

    A a mixture of elements and compounds that have small molecules

    B a mixture of water and ionic compounds

    C a mixture of minerals

- Write the names of up to four elements or compounds in each box. Choose from this list:

oxygen	sodium chloride	silicon dioxide
argon	water	potassium bromide	carbon dioxide
nitrogen	magnesium chloride	aluminium oxide

- Write the symbols for all the substances in the atmosphere box.

1 Atmosphere

2 Hydrosphere

3 Lithosphere

2 Make up 12 sentences using the phrases in the table.

Each sentence must include a phrase from each column.

Write your answers in the grid at the bottom.

For example, the sentence:

Carbon dioxide… never conducts electricity… because…
no ions or electrons can move freely to carry the current.

is

| A | i | 10 |

A Carbon dioxide	a has a high melting point	because	1 the forces of attraction between the molecules are weak.
	b has a low melting point		2 the atoms are held by strong covalent bonds in a giant structure.
B Silicon dioxide	c has a high boiling point		3 it takes a lot of energy to separate its ions to make a gas.
	d has a low boiling point	H	4 there are strong attractive forces between its oppositely charged ions.
	e conducts electricity when it is liquid or dissolved in water		5 there are strong bonds between its positive ions and a 'sea' of negative electrons.
C Sodium chloride			6 its ions are free to move independently.
	f makes crystals		7 its layers of ions can move over each other.
	g is malleable		8 its oppositely charged ions are held together in a three-dimensional pattern.
	h is very hard		
D Copper	i never conducts electricity		9 much energy is needed to break the strong bonds between the atoms.
			10 no ions or electrons can move freely to carry the current.

| A | i | 10 |

C5.1.1–11 What is the atmosphere?

Dry air is a mixture of gases. Our atmosphere is made up of 78% nitrogen, N_2; 21% oxygen, O_2; 1% argon, Ar; 0.04% carbon dioxide, CO_2.

The chemicals of the air consist of atoms and small molecules. There are weak forces of attraction between the molecules. So these chemicals have low melting and boiling points.

Most non-metal elements, and compounds of non-metals, are molecular, with low melting and boiling points.

The atoms in a molecule are joined together by strong **covalent bonds**. A covalent bond is one or more pairs of electrons shared between atoms.

Ⓗ Covalent bonding arises from electrostatic forces of attraction between the shared electrons and the nuclei of the atoms.

Pure molecular compounds cannot conduct electricity. This is because their molecules are not charged.

N≡N
nitrogen molecule

O=O
oxygen molecule

Ar
argon atom

O=C=O
carbon dioxide molecule

C5.2.1–6 What are ionic compounds?

Seawater is a mixture of water and dissolved **ionic compounds**, called salts.

Ionic compounds are made up of positive and negative ions. In ionic solids, the ions are arranged in a **giant three-dimensional lattice** to make crystals. There are very strong attractive forces between the oppositely charged ions. This is ionic bonding.

Ionic compounds have high melting and boiling melting points because much energy is needed to break down an ionic structure.

A solid ionic compound cannot conduct electricity. But when an ionic compound melts, or dissolves in water, its ions are free to move independently. It can now conduct electricity.

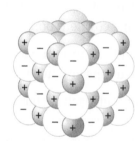
An ionic solid.

C5.2.8–15 How can we identify ions?

There are simple tests to identify ions in compounds. They work because each ion, and each compound, has its own properties.

If you mix certain solutions of ionic compounds, you make an insoluble compound. This forms as a **precipitate**. For example:
- Adding an alkali to a solution that contains Cu^{2+} ions makes a blue precipitate of copper hydroxide:

$$CuCl_2(aq) + 2NaOH(aq) \longrightarrow 2NaCl(aq) + Cu(OH)_2(s)$$

Ⓗ You can summarise the equation above with an ionic equation, which shows only the ions that take part in the reaction:

$$Cu^{2+}(aq) + 2OH^-(aq) \longrightarrow Cu(OH)_2(s)$$

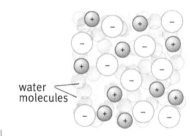
water molecules
A solution of an ionic compound in water.

C
5

Solutions containing some other metal ions also react with alkalis in solution to make precipitates.

*   Adding acidified silver nitrate solution to a solution of Cl^- ions makes a white precipitate of silver chloride:

$$AgNO_3(aq) + NaCl(aq) \longrightarrow AgCl(s) + NaNO_3(aq)$$

$$Ag^+(aq) + Cl^-(aq) \longrightarrow AgCl(s)$$

There are tests to identify other negative ions.

H You can use solubility data to predict chemicals that will precipitate on mixing solutions. A compound with a low solubility will form as a precipitate. If both products are soluble, no precipitate will form.

C5.3.1–8 What are giant structures?

The **lithosphere** is the Earth's rigid outer layer. It consists of the crust and part of the mantle. It is a mixture of **minerals**. Minerals are compounds that occur naturally.

Silicon, oxygen, and aluminium are the most common elements in the Earth's crust. Much of the silicon and oxygen exists as a compound, silicon dioxide. Solid silicon dioxide has a **giant structure** of atoms. Its atoms are held together in a huge lattice by strong covalent bonds.

Diamond and graphite are also minerals. They both consist of carbon atoms arranged in giant structures.

In diamond, each carbon atom is joined to four other carbon atoms by strong covalent bonds. The four bonds are arranged in three dimensions around each carbon atom.

In graphite, each carbon atom is joined to three others by strong covalent bonds. The three bonds are arranged around each carbon atom, making sheets of hexagons. Between the sheets, or layers, are free electrons. These help to stick the layers together.

The structures of diamond, graphite, and silicon dioxide explain their properties and uses.

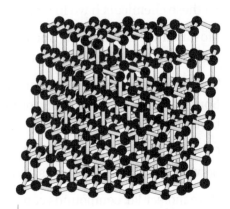
○ A model of the structure of diamond.

○ A model of the structure of graphite.

	Graphite	Diamond	Silicon dioxide
Melting and boiling points	Very high because much energy is needed to break the strong covalent bonds in the giant structure of atoms.		
Solubility in water	Insoluble because much energy is needed to break the strong covalent bonds.		
Hardness	Soft because the forces between the layers are weak. A good lubricant.	Very hard because much energy is needed to break the strong covalent bonds between the surface atoms. Diamond is useful for cutting tools and drill tips.	
Electrical conductivity	Good because the electrons between the layers are free to move.	Do not conduct electricity because there are no charged particles free to move.	

C5.4.23–25 Why are metals useful?

Metals have many uses. Their uses depend on their properties. Metals have high melting points, and they are:

*   **malleable** – they bend without breaking
*   strong
*   good electrical conductors.

Solid metals have giant crystalline structures. Strong **metallic bonds** hold the atoms together. This explains why metals are strong and why they have high melting points.

Ⓗ A metal crystal is made up of positive metal ions arranged in layers. When you bend a metal, the layers of ions slide over each other. The ions are held together by a sea of electrons that are free to move. When a metal wire conducts electricity, electrons drift from one end towards the other.

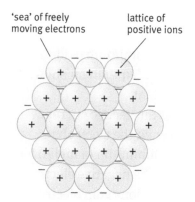

'sea' of freely moving electrons   lattice of positive ions

A model of metallic bonding.

C5.4.1–5, 5.4.11–22 How are metals extracted?

In the lithosphere, most metals are joined to other elements in **minerals**. Rocks that contain useful minerals are called **ores**. Copper is extracted from the mineral copper iron sulfide ($CuFeS_2$). The ore that contains this mineral is copper pyrites.

Ores contain different amounts of minerals. Often, a huge amount of ore contains only a tiny mass of a useful mineral.

The method used to extract a metal from its ore depends on the metal's reactivity.

Extracting metals by heating with carbon

Iron, copper, and zinc are extracted from their oxides by heating with carbon. For example:

$$\text{zinc oxide} + \text{carbon} \longrightarrow \text{zinc} + \text{carbon monoxide}$$
$$ZnO(s) + C(s) \longrightarrow Zn(l) + CO(g)$$

Zinc oxide loses oxygen. It is **reduced**. Carbon gains oxygen. It is **oxidised**.

Extracting metals by electrolysis

Reactive metals, like aluminium, are joined very strongly to other elements in minerals. They cannot be extracted by heating with carbon. So they are extracted by **electrolysis**.

Aluminium oxide is an ionic compound. When it melts, its ions can move independently. So liquid aluminium oxide conducts electricity. It is an **electrolyte**. Electrolytes break down, or **decompose**, when an electric current passes through them. This is **electrolysis**.

Ⓗ You can calculate the mass of a metal in a mineral. For example:

What is the mass of aluminium in 100 kg of aluminium oxide, Al_2O_3?

*   Use the periodic table to find out the relative atomic masses of the elements in the mineral:
    Al = 27 and O = 16
*   Calculate the mineral's relative formula mass:
    $(27 \times 2) + (16 \times 3) = 102$
*   Calculate the relative mass of the metal in the formula:
    $27 \times 2 = 54$
*   Calculate the mass of metal in 1 kg of the mineral:
    $54 \div 102 \text{ kg} = 0.53 \text{ kg}$
*   Multiply by 100 to find the mass of metal in 100 kg of the mineral:
    $0.53 \text{ kg} \times 100 = 53 \text{ kg}$

C 5

To extract aluminium from aluminium oxide:

- Melt aluminium oxide. Pour it into the equipment shown on the right:
- Pass an electric current through the electrolyte.
  - Aluminium (a metal) forms at the negative electrode. Al^{3+} ions gain electrons from the electrode to make neutral aluminium atoms:
  $$Al^{3+} + 3e^- \longrightarrow Al$$
  - Oxygen (a non-metal) forms at the positive electrode. O^{2-} ions give electrons to the positive electrode to make oxygen atoms:
  $$O^{2-} \longrightarrow O + 2e^-$$
  Oxygen atoms then join together to make oxygen molecules:
  $$O + O \longrightarrow O_2$$

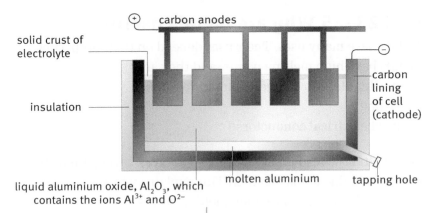

carbon anodes

solid crust of electrolyte

insulation

carbon lining of cell (cathode)

liquid aluminium oxide, Al_2O_3, which contains the ions Al^{3+} and O^{2-}

molten aluminium

tapping hole

Electrolysis cell for the extraction of aluminium. You do not need to learn the details of this for the exam.

C5.4.26 What are the environmental impacts of using metals?

Use extra paper to answer these questions if you need to.

1 Use the data in the table to answer the questions.

Element	% by mass of element in lithosphere	% by volume of element in atmosphere
Aluminium	8	0
argon	0	1
iron	5	0
nitrogen	0	78
oxygen	47	21
silicon	28	0

a Name the most abundant element in the lithosphere.

b Name the most abundant element in the atmosphere.

c Name the element that is abundant in both the atmosphere and the lithosphere.

d Name the most abundant non-metal element in the lithosphere.

e Name the most abundant metal in the lithosphere.

2 Draw lines to match each formula to a diagram.

CO_2 **A**

H_2O **B**

O_2 **C**

Ar **D**

3 Use words from the box to fill in the gaps. Each word may be used once, more than once, or not at all.

> **three cannot carbon covalent**
>
> **silicon four slippery hard**
>
> **can lubricant abrasive**

Diamond and graphite are two forms of the element _____. Diamond and graphite have giant _____ structures. In diamond, each atom is joined to _____ others by strong _____ bonds. These bonds mean that diamond is very _____. In graphite, each atom is joined to _____ others by strong _____ bonds to form layers. These layers can slide over each other, making graphite _____. This means it is a good _____. Graphite has electrons drifting between its layers, so it _____ conduct electricity.

4 Write word equations for the reactions below.

a zinc oxide reacting with carbon to make zinc and carbon dioxide

b copper oxide reacting with carbon

5 For each equation below, circle in **red** the reactant that is reduced. Circle in **blue** the reactant that is oxidised.

a iron oxide + carbon $\longrightarrow$ iron + carbon dioxide

b tin oxide + carbon $\longrightarrow$ tin + carbon dioxide

6 The stages below describe how aluminium is extracted from bauxite ore. They are in the wrong order.

A Add sodium hydroxide solution to remove impurities from the bauxite.

B Pass an electric current through the aluminium oxide.

C Melt the aluminium oxide.

D Aluminium forms at the negative electrode and oxygen forms at the positive electrode.

E Collect liquid aluminium from the tapping hole at the bottom of the tank.

Fill in the boxes to show the right order. The first one has been done for you.

A				

7 Draw lines to match each substance with its **type of structure** and its **melting point**. One has been done for you.

Substance	Type of structure	Boiling point (°C)
nitrogen	giant covalent	4830
silicon dioxide	giant ionic	−196
sodium chloride	giant covalent	2230
graphite	simple covalent	1413

H 8 Balance the equations below.

a $ZnO(s) + C(s) \longrightarrow Zn(l) + CO_2(g)$

b $Fe_2O_3(s) + C(s) \longrightarrow Fe(l) + CO_2(g)$

c $CuO(s) + C(s) \longrightarrow Cu(l) + CO_2(g)$

9 Write ionic equations, including state symbols, for:

a the reaction of lead nitrate solution with potassium iodide solution to make a precipitate of lead iodide, PbI_2

b the reaction of copper(II) chloride solution with sodium hydroxide solution to make a precipitate of copper hydroxide, $Cu(OH)_2$.

10 Calculate the mass of the metal in:

a 162 tonnes of zinc oxide, ZnO

b 51 kg of aluminium oxide, Al_2O_3.

C 5

1 Sarah needs to identify two white salts, A and B. She does the tests in the table opposite.

Test number	Test	Salt A observations	Salt B observations
1	Dissolve a little of the salt in water. Add a small volume of sodium hydroxide solution.	white precipitate	white precipitate
2	Add more sodium hydroxide solution.	no change	precipitate dissolves
3	Add hydrochloric acid to the solid.	no change	no change
4	Dissolve a little of the salt in water. Add dilute nitric acid, then barium nitrate solution.	no change	white precipitate
5	Add dilute nitric acid, then silver nitrate solution.	cream precipitate	no change

a Give the formula of the metal ion present in salt B.

_____ [1]

b Which of the two salts is a sulfate?

_____ [1]

c Give the name of salt A. Explain how you work out your answer.

_____

_____ [2]

> **Exam tip**
>
> You do not have to remember the results of the tests for ions – you will be given a data sheet to help you.

d Explain why nitric acid is added in test 5, and not hydrochloric acid.

_____

_____ [2]

e Silver ions (Ag^+) react with chloride ions (Cl^-) to make silver chloride precipitate.

Write an ionic equation for this reaction.

Include state symbols.

_____ [2]

Total [8]

2 Many dental drills are made from diamond.

Diamond is a form of the element carbon.

Explain why the properties of diamond make it a suitable material for drill tips.

Use your knowledge and understanding of the structure and bonding of diamond to explain why diamond has these properties.

The quality of written communication will be assessed in your answer to this question.

Write your answer on separate paper or in your exercise book.

Total [6]

3 a The bar chart shows the melting points of four substances.

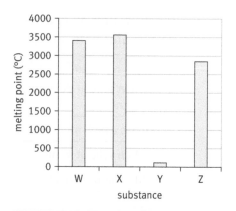

    i Substance Y exists as small molecules.
Explain how the data on the bar chart show this.

_____ [1]

    ii Which of the elements below could be substance Y?
Use the periodic table to help you decide.
Draw a (ring) around the correct answer.

       magnesium   iodine   technetium   antimony   [1]

b The table gives more data for substances W, X, and Z.

    i Which of the substances in the table might have a
giant covalent structure?

    Give a reason for your decision.

_____

_____ [1]

Substance	Does it conduct electricity when solid?
W	yes
X	no
Z	no

    ii Suggest what further data you would need to help you
decide which of the substances in the table is an ionic
compound.

    Explain how this extra data would help you to make
your decision.

_____

_____ [2]

c One of the substances in the table is tungsten.

    i Use the periodic table to help you identify which
substance is tungsten. Draw a (ring) around the
correct answer.

       substance W   substance X   substance Z   [1]

    ii Tungsten is used to make electrodes for electrolysis.
Give one property of tungsten that makes it suitable
for this purpose.

_____ [1]

Total [7]

4 a Magnesium bromide is an ionic compound.

It used to be used as a sedative. It is also a laxative.

    i In which 'sphere' are many ionic compounds found
dissolved in water?

    Tick one box.

       lithosphere   ☐
       atmosphere   ☐
       hydrosphere   ☐ [1]

C 5

ii Draw lines to match each property of magnesium bromide with a reason.

Property		Reason
When solid, it does not conduct electricity.		There are very strong attractive forces between the positive and negative ions.
It has a high melting point.		The ions are arranged in a regular pattern.
When solid, it forms crystals.		The charged particles cannot move.
When liquid, it conducts electricity.		The charged particles can move independently.

[3]

Ⓗ

iii Magnesium bromide contains these ions:

Mg^{2+} and Br^-

What is the formula of magnesium bromide? _____ [2]

b In World War Two, magnesium was extracted from seawater to make bombs.

The mass of magnesium ions in 1 m³ of seawater is 1.3 kg.

Calculate the volume of seawater that contains 100 kg of magnesium ions.

Answer = _____ [2]

c i Today, magnesium metal is manufactured by the electrolysis of liquid magnesium chloride.

Which statements correctly describe what happens during this process?

Tick the correct two boxes.

Liquid magnesium metal forms at the positive electrode. ☐

An electric current decomposes the electrolyte. ☐

An electric current passes through liquid magnesium chloride. ☐

Chlorine gas is made at the negative electrode. ☐ [2]

ii Explain why magnesium cannot be produced by heating magnesium oxide with carbon.

_____ [1]

Total [11]

5 Serotonin is a hormone. It carries messages in the human body. Changes in the amount of serotonin in a person's brain may affect their mood. The chemical formula of serotonin is $C_{10}H_{12}N_2O$.

a Calculate the relative formula mass of serotonin.

Show clearly how you work out your answer.

Relative atomic masses: H = 1; C = 12; N = 14; O = 16

_____

_____ [2]

> **Exam tip**
>
> Write out calculations carefully before you do them. Then check your working, and your answer.

b The chemical dopamine also carries messages in the brain.

Its formula is $C_6H_{11}NO_2$.

The relative formula mass of dopamine is 153.

Calculate the mass of nitrogen in 153 g of dopamine.

Show clearly how you work out your answer.

_____

_____ [2]

Total [4]

6 The lithosphere contains large amounts of silicon dioxide.

a Finish the sentences about the structure of silicon dioxide.

Choose words from this list.

| simple | giant | weak | strong |

Silicon dioxide has a _____ covalent structure.

Its atoms are held together by _____ covalent bonds. [2]

b This is a list of properties of silicon dioxide.

A It has a high boiling point.

B Solid and liquid silicon dioxide do not conduct electricity.

C It is very hard.

D It is insoluble in water.

E It has a high melting point.

C 5

Which properties best explain the following facts about silicon dioxide?

Choose from the letters **A, B, C, D,** and **E**.

i   Silicon dioxide is used as an abrasive to make surfaces smooth.

_____ [1]

ii   Silicon dioxide is used to line furnaces that heat things to very high temperatures.

_____ [1]

Total [4]

Going for the highest grades

7 Aluminium is used to make overhead power lines.

a   **i**   Draw a labelled diagram in the space below to represent the bonding in aluminium metal.

[2]

ii   Use your diagram to explain why aluminium is a good conductor of electricity, and why it is malleable.

_____
_____
_____ [2]

b   Aluminium is extracted from bauxite.
Bauxite is mainly aluminium oxide, Al_2O_3.

i   Calculate the mass of aluminium that can be extracted from 1000 tonnes of aluminium oxide.

_____
_____
_____ [3]

ii   Describe how aluminium is extracted from aluminium oxide by electrolysis. In your answer, include a description of what happens at each electrode.

The quality of written communication will be assessed in your answer to this question.

Write your answer on separate paper, or in your exercise book.

[6]

Total [13]

1 Fill in the gaps.

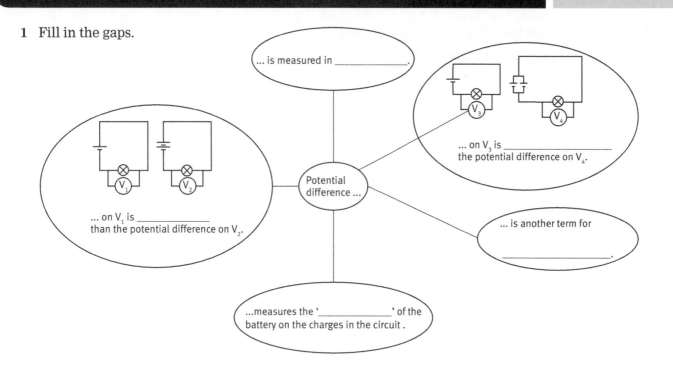

... is measured in _____.

... on V_3 is _____
the potential difference on V_4.

... on V_1 is _____
than the potential difference on V_2.

Potential
difference ...

... is another term for

_____.

...measures the '_____' of the
battery on the charges in the circuit .

2

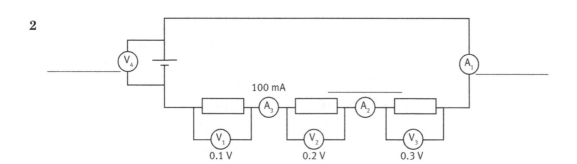

100 mA

A_3 _____ A_2

V_1 V_2 V_3

0.1 V   0.2 V   0.3 V

a   On the diagram, write the readings on ammeters A_1 and A_2.

b   i   On the diagram, draw a (ring) around the resistor
that has the greatest resistance.

   ii   Draw a (ring) around the correct bold word below.
Then complete the sentence.

The potential difference is **smallest / greatest** across
the component with the greatest resistance because

_____

c   i   On the diagram, write the reading on voltmeter V_4.

   ii   Complete the sentence:
I know that this is the voltage on V_4 because _____

_____

_____

Exam tip

Before you answer a question
about a circuit, check whether
the components are connected
in series or in parallel.

**P
5**

3 In the six circuits below, all the lamps are identical.

For each pair of circuits, draw a (ring) around the circuit in which the ammeter reading is greater.

a

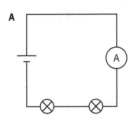

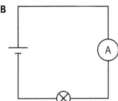

b

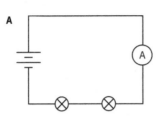

c

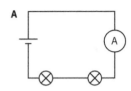

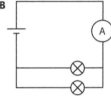

4 Solve the clues to fill in the arrow words.

1 →								2 ↓	
3 →		4 →						5 →	
					← 6		16 ↓	
7 →								
8 →							← 9	
10 →							11→	
12 →				13 →		14→	
15 →								

Horizontal

1 Divide the voltage by the current to calculate this.

3 The unit of resistance.

4 The rate at which a power supply transfers energy to an appliance.

5 The symbol for the unit of potential difference.

6 In this type of circuit, the current through each component is the same as if it were the only component.

7 Use this device to measure potential difference across a component in a circuit.

8 The symbol for the unit of resistance.

9 This device consists of a magnet rotating within a coil of wire.

10 Generators produce electricity by electromagnetic _____

11 The symbol for resistance.

12 Batteries produce _____ current.

13 This type of current reverses direction several times a second.

14 The symbol for the unit of electric current.

15 In a motor, a _____ reverses the direction of the current in the coil at an appropriate point in each revolution.

Vertical

2 A flow of charge.

16 The abbreviation for direct current is _____.

P5.1.1–4 What is static electricity?

If you rub a balloon in your hair, the balloon and your hair become charged. Tiny negative particles (electrons) move from your hair to the balloon.

Each hair is positively charged. Like charges repel. So the hairs get as far away from each other as possible.

There are attractive forces between opposite charges, so positively charged hairs are attracted to the negatively charged balloon.

P5.1.5–10 What is an electric current?

Electric current is a flow of charge.

Metal conductors have many charges (electrons) that are free to move. Electric current is the movement of these free electrons. Insulators do not conduct electricity. This is because they have very few charges that are free to move.

The components and wires conduct electricity when the switch is closed and the circuit is complete.

The battery makes free charges move in a continuous loop. The free charges are not used up.

The ammeter measures electric current in amperes, or amps (A).

P5.2.5–7 What is electrical power?

When an electric charge flows through a component or device in a circuit, work is done by the power supply. Energy is transferred from the power supply to the component and its surroundings.

Power is a measure of the rate at which an electrical power supply transfers energy to an appliance or device, and its surroundings.

You can use the equation below to calculate power:

power = **voltage** × **current**
(watts, W) (volts, V) (amperes, A)

Components resist the flow of charge through them.

variable   filament   motor   fixed
resistor   lamp   resistor

power supply
In a given circuit, the bigger the voltage, the bigger the current.

The resistance of the connecting wires is tiny, so you can usually ignore it.

P5.2.1–4, P5.2.8–16 Resistance?

The bigger the resistance, the smaller the current.
The current through a metal conductor is proportional to the voltage across it:

$$\text{resistance (ohm, } \Omega) = \frac{\text{voltage (volt, V)}}{\text{current (ampere, A)}}$$

The gradient of the graph is constant. It is equal to the resistance of the resistor.

Resistors get hotter when electric current passes through them. This happens because moving electrons bump into stationary ions in the wire.

Lamp filaments get so hot that they glow.

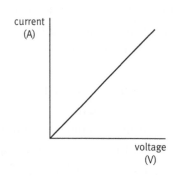

current (A)

voltage (V)

Two resistors in **series** have more resistance than one on its own. The battery must push charges through both resistors.

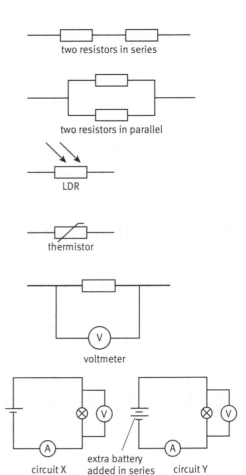

two resistors in series

Two resistors in **parallel** have a smaller total resistance than one on its own. There are more paths for electric charges to flow along.

two resistors in parallel

The resistance of a light-dependent resistor (**LDR**) changes with light intensity. Its resistance in the dark is greater than its resistance in the light. LDRs switch outdoor lights on at night.

LDR

The resistance of a **thermistor** changes with temperature. For many thermistors, the hotter the temperature, the lower the resistance. Thermistors switch water heaters on and off.

thermistor

5.3.1–7 How do series and parallel circuits work?

The **voltage** of a battery shows its 'push' on the charges in a circuit. **Potential difference (p.d.)** means the same as voltage.

voltmeter

The greater the potential difference between two points in a circuit, the more work must be done to make a given amount of charge move between the points.

You can use a **voltmeter** to measure the potential difference across a component in a circuit. The diagram (above right) shows how to connect it.

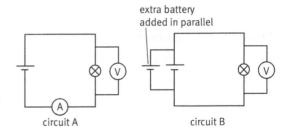

circuit X   extra battery added in series   circuit Y

The readings on the voltmeter and ammeter are greater in circuit Y than in circuit X (see right). The second battery gives an extra 'push' to the charges in the circuit.

H The readings on the voltmeter and ammeter are the same in circuits A and B (see right). The second battery provides no extra 'push' to the charges in the circuit.

extra battery added in parallel

circuit A   circuit B

In circuit S:

- Three components are connected in series to a battery.
- The same current flows through each component.
- The potential differences across the components add up to the potential difference across the battery.

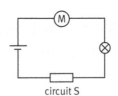

circuit S

- **H** This is because the work done on each unit of charge by the battery must equal the work done by it on the circuit components.
- The potential difference is biggest across the component with the greatest resistance.
- **H** This is because a charge flowing through a big resistance does more work than a charge flowing through a smaller resistance.
- If you change the resistance of one of the components, there will be a change in the potential differences across all the components.

In circuit P:

- Three components are connected in parallel to a battery.
- The current at J, and at K, is equal to the sum of the currents through the components.
- The current is largest through the component with the smallest resistance.
- **(H)** This is because the same battery voltage pushes more current through a component with a smaller resistance than through one with a bigger resistance.
- The current through each component is the same as if it were the only component.
- The p.d. across each component is the same as p.d. of the battery.

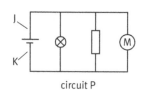

circuit P

P5.4.3–5 What is electromagnetic induction?

If you move a magnet into a coil of wire, a voltage is induced across the ends of the coil (diagram A). This is **electromagnetic induction**. If you join up the ends of the coil to make a circuit, a current flows.

You can induce a voltage in the opposite direction by:
- moving the magnet *out* of the coil (diagram B) or
- moving the *other pole of* the magnet into the coil (diagram C).

P5.4.1–2, P5.4.11–16 How is mains electricity generated?

Generators make electricity by electromagnetic induction. In a generator, a magnet or electromagnet turns near a coil of wire.

This induces a voltage across the ends of the coil.
The direction of this voltage changes each time the magnet rotates.

You can increase the size of the induced voltage by:
- turning the magnet faster
- making the magnetic field stronger
- adding more turns to the coil
- putting an iron core inside the coil.

Alternating current

(H) The magnet in a generator turns all the time. Its magnetic field constantly changes direction. So the direction of the induced current changes all the time. This is an **alternating current (a.c.)**. The current from a battery is always in the same direction. It is a **direct current (d.c.)**.

Mains electricity is supplied as an alternating current (a.c.).

(H) This is because:
- it is easier to generate than d.c.
- it can be distributed more efficiently, with less energy wasted as heat.

In the UK, domestic mains electricity is supplied at 230 volts.

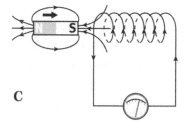

A

sensitive ammeter

B

C

rotate magnet

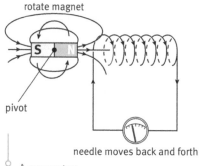

pivot

needle moves back and forth

A generator.

Alternating current.

P5.4.6–10 What are transformers?

If the current in a coil of wire changes, its magnetic field also changes. The changing magnetic field induces a voltage in a nearby coil.

A transformer consists of two coils of wire wound onto an iron core. It changes the size of an alternating voltage.

H The changing current in one coil of the transformer causes a changing magnetic field in the iron core. This induces a changing potential difference across the other transformer coil.

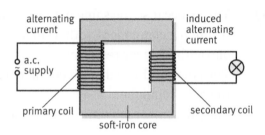

You can use this equation to work out the size of the voltage across the secondary coil:

$$\frac{\text{voltage across primary coil}}{\text{voltage across secondary coil}} = \frac{\text{number of turns on primary coil}}{\text{number of turns on secondary coil}}$$

P5.5.1–6 How are electric motors made?

If a current is flowing through a wire or coil, the wire or coil can exert a force on:

- a nearby permanent magnet
- another current-carrying coil or wire nearby.

For a current-carrying wire in a magnetic field:

- If the magnet's lines of force are at 90° to the wire, the wire experiences a force at 90° to both the current direction and the lines of force of the field.
- If the magnet's lines of force are parallel to the wire, the wire experiences no force.

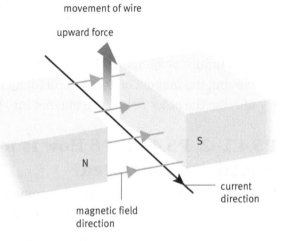

The diagram opposite shows how the **motor effect** results in a turning force on a rectangular coil in a uniform magnetic field. If you add a **commutator** to the setup opposite, the coil rotates continuously. This happens because the commutator swaps the current direction every time the coil is vertical.

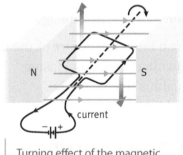
Turning effect of the magnetic forces on a flat coil.

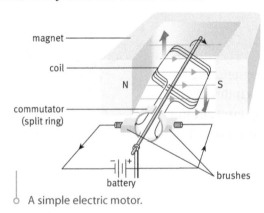
A simple electric motor.

Motors are used in computer hard disk drives, DVD players, and electric motor vehicles.

Use extra paper to answer these questions if you need to.

1 Draw the symbols for the components below.
   a ammeter
   b voltmeter
   c cell
   d power supply
   e filament lamp
   f switch
   g light-dependent resistor (LDR)
   h fixed resistor
   i variable resistor
   j thermistor

2 Use the sentence beginnings and endings to write eight full sentences.

Beginnings	Endings
All conductors	do not conduct electricity.
Metal conductors	include polythene, wood, and rubber.
Insulators	charges are not used up.
In a complete circuit	the battery makes free charges flow in a continuous loop.
	contain charges that are free to move.
	contain electrons that are free to move.
	do not contain charges that are free to move.

3 Highlight the correct word in each pair of **bold** words. Resistors get **colder/hotter** when electric current flows through them. This is why lamp filaments glow.
The resistance of a light-dependent resistor changes with light intensity. Its resistance in the dark is **less/more** than its resistance in the light. The resistance of a thermistor changes with temperature. Usually, the higher the temperature, the **smaller/bigger** the resistance.

4 Write **X** next to the statements that are true for circuit X below. Write **Y** next to the statements that are true for circuit Y. Write **B** next to the statements that are true for both circuits.

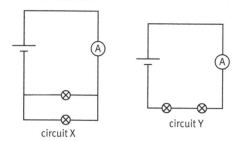
circuit X
circuit Y

   a There are several paths for the current.
   b This circuit has a greater total resistance.
   c The ammeter reading is smaller for this circuit.
   d The components resist the flow of charge.
   e The resistance of the connecting wires is so small that you can ignore it.
   f It is easier for the battery to push charges around this circuit.

5 Fill in the gaps.

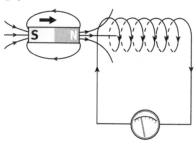

If you move the magnet into the coil of wire, a voltage is induced across the ends of the _____. If you connect the ends of the coil to make a closed circuit, a _____ flows round the circuit.
You can induce a voltage in the opposite direction by moving the magnet _____ of the coil or by moving the other _____ of the magnet into the coil.

6 A graph shows how the voltage produced by a generator changes with time when the magnet spins at a particular speed.

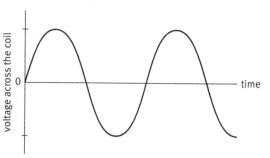

Sketch a graph to show what happens when the magnet is spun around more quickly.

7 Calculate the power of these appliances. Assume the voltage is 230 V.
   a a vacuum cleaner with a current of 4 A flowing through it
   b a DVD player with a current of 0.9 A flowing through it

H 8 primary coil : 1000 turns   secondary coil : 50 turns

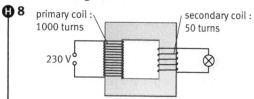

230 V

Calculate the voltage across the secondary coil.

9 Explain why:
   a Resistors get hotter when an electric current flows through them.
   b In a series circuit, the potential difference is largest across the component with the greatest resistance.
   c Mains electricity is supplied as a.c.

P 5

1   Tamara has a portable heater. She plugs it into a car battery.

She puts the heating element into a mug of water to make a hot drink.

a   Tamara wants to find out more about her heater.

She connects this circuit.

i   Tamara uses a voltmeter to measure the voltage across the heater.

Draw on the diagram to show where to connect the voltmeter.

Use the correct symbol.   [1]

ii   The reading on the voltmeter is 12 V. The ammeter reads 10 A.

Calculate the resistance of the heater.

Resistance = _____ ohms   [2]

b   The heater contains a heating element made from a coil of wire.

The wire gets hotter when an electric current passes through it.

Explain why the wire gets hotter.

_____

_____ [2]

Total [5]

2   When a current flows in the circuit opposite, the coil rotates continuously. Explain why.

The quality of written communication will be assessed in your answer to this question.
Write your answer on separate paper or in your exercise book.

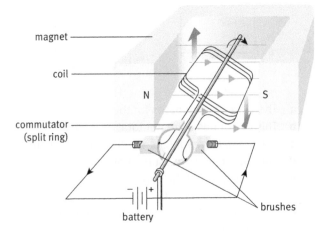

Total [6]

3 Scientists have invented a wind-up laptop computer. School students will use it in places where electricity supplies are not reliable.

A person turns a handle for 1 minute. This winds up a spring.

Then the spring unwinds slowly. This rotates a magnet within a coil of wire.

This generator produces an electric current.

a Suggest three changes the scientists could make to the generator so that it produced a bigger current.

Change 1: _____

Change 2: _____

Change 3: _____ [3]

H b The computer can also be plugged into the mains electricity supply.

A transformer changes the size of the voltage.

12 V laptop

i Explain how the transformer works.

_____

_____

_____ [2]

ii Coil P has 2300 turns.

Calculate the number of turns needed in coil S to give a voltage of 12 V across the computer.

Answer = _____ [2]

Total [7]

4 The diagram shows part of an electric circuit in Matt's house.

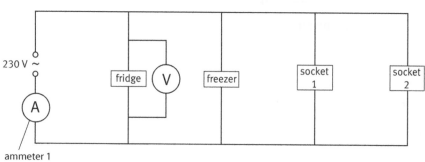

P 5

a **i** What is the reading on the voltmeter connected across the fridge?

_____ [1]

ii What is the potential difference across the fridge?

_____ [1]

b The resistance of the freezer is 70 Ω.

The voltage across the freezer is 230 V.

Calculate the current through the freezer.

Current = _____ amps [2]

c Matt plugs a kettle into socket 1.

What happens to the size the current through the freezer?

Draw a (ring) around the correct answer.

increases   **decreases**   **stays the same**   [1]

d Matt plugs a kettle into socket 1 and an electric heater into socket 2.

He switches off the freezer.

He measures the currents through the appliances that are switched on.

Appliance	Current (A)
fridge	0.4
kettle	5.0
heater	9.0

i What current flows through ammeter 1?

Current = _____ amps [2]

ii Which appliance in the table has the greatest resistance?

_____ [1]

Give a reason for your answer.

_____

_____ [1]

Total [9]

5 Vanessa has four resistors.

She sets up an experiment to measure the resistance of each one.

She records one value of voltage and one value of current for each resistor.

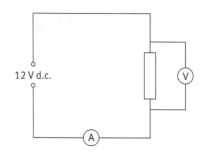

12 V d.c.

Resistor	Voltage (V)	Current (A)	Resistance (Ω)
J	12	4	
K	12	0.4	
L	12	0.2	
M	12	6	

a Use data from the table to calculate the resistance of each resistor.
Write your answers in the table above.   [2]

b Vanessa gives Ursula one of her four resistors.

Ursula records the current that flows through the resistor at each of five different voltages.

She plots the values on the graph opposite.

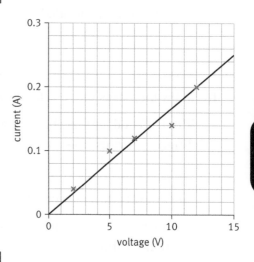

i Use the graph to calculate the resistance of the resistor.

Use the equation below and show your working.
Include the unit in your answer.

$$\text{resistance of resistor} = \frac{1}{\text{gradient of the graph}}$$

_____   [2]

ii From which resistor (J, K, L, or M) did Ursula obtain the data shown on the graph?

_____   [1]

c The graph opposite is for resistor M.

Explain how the graph increases or decreases your confidence that the resistance you calculated for resistor M in part is correct.

_____
_____   [2]

Total [7]

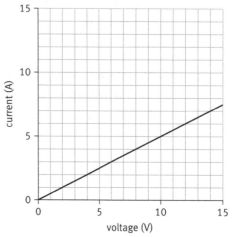

P 5

Going for the highest grades

6 Mary sets up the circuit opposite.

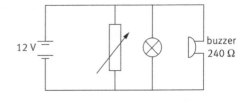

a What is the current through the lamp?

_____ [1]

b Explain why the total potential difference across the three components of the circuit add up to the potential difference across the battery.

_____

_____

_____

_____ [2]

c Which component in the circuit has the greatest resistance?

Explain how you decided.

_____

_____ [1]

d Mary increases the resistance of the variable resistor.

What effect does this change have on the potential difference across the buzzer?

_____ [1]

e Edward sets up a new circuit with the same components.

He moves the slider on the variable resistor back to its original position, before Mary moved it.

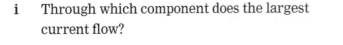

i Through which component does the largest current flow?

_____ [1]

ii Explain why the current through the component you identified in part i is greater than the currents that flow through the other components in Edward's circuit.

_____

_____ [2]

Total [8]

1 Match each word with its definition.

Word	Definition
behaviour	a change in the environment
stimulus	an action caused by a change in the environment
response	anything an animal does

2 The diagram shows a reflex arc. Use these words to label the diagram.

> **receptor**   **sensory neuron**   **spinal cord**
>
> **motor neuron**   **effector**

Exam tip

Make sure you can label a reflex arc – they often come up in exam questions.

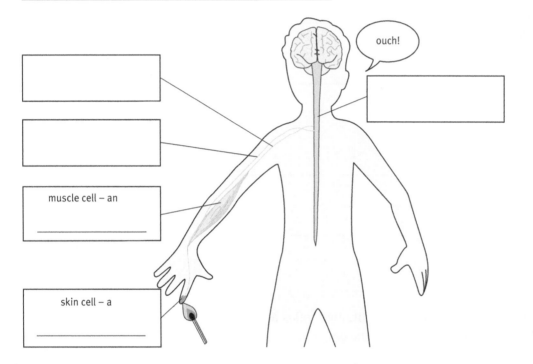

muscle cell – an

_____

skin cell – a

_____

ouch!

3 The diagram shows a motor neuron.
  Complete the labels to describe what each part of the cell does.

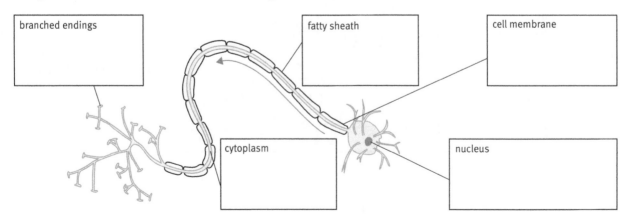

branched endings

fatty sheath

cell membrane

cytoplasm

nucleus

4   The diagrams show how a nerve impulse crosses a synapse.
They are in the wrong order.
- Number each box to show the correct sequence.
- Write notes next to each diagram to explain the process.

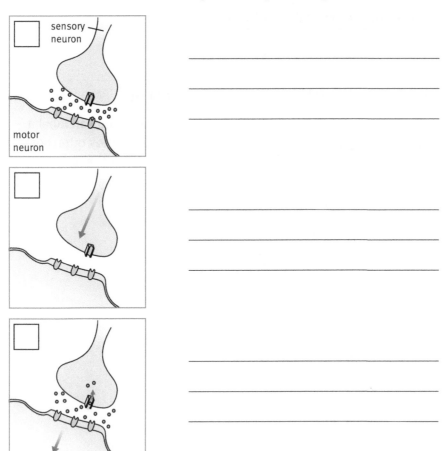

_____

_____

_____

_____

_____

_____

_____

_____

_____

5   The cartoon shows the benefits of one conditioned reflex action.
Complete the thought bubbles to describe the benefits.

B6.1.1 How do animals respond to changes?

You are at a party. The room gets hotter. You sweat more.
A change in your environment, or **stimulus** (temperature
increase), has triggered a **response** (more sweating).

B6.1.2–5 What are simple reflex actions?

Simple reflex actions happen quickly. They are **involuntary**
(automatic).

Simple animals rely on reflex actions for most of their behaviour.
So they always respond in the same way to a particular stimulus.
Woodlice move away from light, for example.

Reflex actions help simple animals respond to stimuli in ways
that help them survive, including finding food and hiding
from predators.

A human baby shows **newborn reflexes**, including:
* **grasping** – tightly gripping a finger in her palm
* **sucking** a nipple or finger in her mouth
* **stepping** when her feet touch a flat surface.

Adults show reflex actions, too. For example:
* The **pupil reflex** stops light damaging cells in your retina.
  In bright light, some of the muscles in your iris contract.
  Your pupil gets smaller, so less light enters your eye.
* If someone hits your leg just below the knee, your thigh
  muscle contracts and your leg straightens. This is the **knee
  jerk reflex**.
* If you pick up something hot, you drop it before you feel it.

B6.1.6–10 How do we respond to stimuli?

To respond to stimuli, an animal needs:
* **Receptors** to detect stimuli. These include:
  - single cells, such as pain sensor cells in the skin
  - cells in complex organs, for example, cells in the retina.
* **Processing centres** to receive information and co-ordinate
  responses.
* **Effectors** to respond to stimuli. These include:
  - **muscle cells**, which contract to move a part of the body
  - **glands**, whose cells release chemical **hormones**.

As multicellular organisms evolved, their bodies developed
complex nervous and hormonal communication systems.
* **Nerve impulses** are electrical signals. They bring about fast,
  short-lived responses.
* **Hormones** travel in the blood. They cause slower, longer-
  lasting responses, for example:
  - The pancreas makes **insulin** to control blood sugar.
  - **Oestrogen** helps to control the female menstrual cycle.

**B
6**

B6.2.1–10 How does the nervous system work?

In the nervous system, **neurons** (nerve cells) link receptor cells to effector cells. Neurons transmit electrical impulses when stimulated.

A neuron has an **axon**. This is a long extension of the cytoplasm. It is surrounded by a cell membrane. Some axons are surrounded by a **fatty sheath**. This insulates the neuron from nearby cells, so electrical signals can pass along it quickly.

In humans and other vertebrates, the **central nervous system** (CNS) is made up of the spinal cord and brain. The CNS coordinates an animal's responses to stimuli.

The **peripheral nervous system** (PNS) links the CNS to the rest of the body. It is made up of sensory and motor neurons.

In a simple reflex, impulses move from one part of the nervous system to the next in a **reflex arc**.

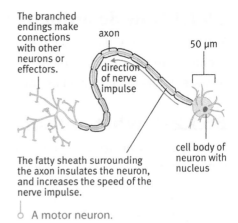

The branched endings make connections with other neurons or effectors.

axon

50 μm

direction of nerve impulse

The fatty sheath surrounding the axon insulates the neuron, and increases the speed of the nerve impulse.

cell body of neuron with nucleus

A motor neuron.

CENTRAL NERVOUS SYSTEM (CNS) { the brain, spinal cord

Sensory and motor neurons link the CNS to the body.

PERIPHERAL NERVOUS SYSTEM (PNS)

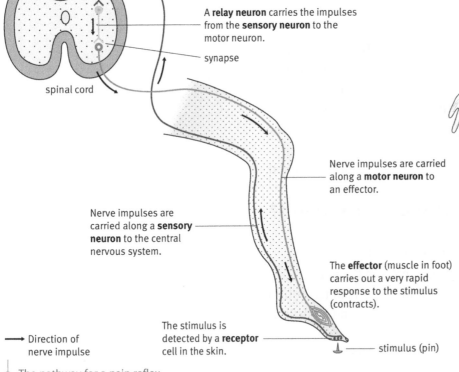

A **relay neuron** carries the impulses from the **sensory neuron** to the motor neuron.

synapse

spinal cord

Nerve impulses are carried along a **motor neuron** to an effector.

Nerve impulses are carried along a **sensory neuron** to the central nervous system.

The **effector** (muscle in foot) carries out a very rapid response to the stimulus (contracts).

→ Direction of nerve impulse

The stimulus is detected by a **receptor** cell in the skin.

stimulus (pin)

The pathway for a pain reflex.

H In a reflex arc, the neurons are arranged in a fixed pathway. Information does not need to be processed, so responses are automatic. This makes reflex responses very quick.

B6.2.11–13 What are synapses?

There are tiny gaps (**synapses**) between neurons in a reflex arc. Nerve impulses must cross these gaps to get from one neuron to the next. Special chemicals pass impulses across synapses.

Ⓗ These chemicals are called **transmitter substances**. The diagrams show how they work.

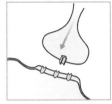

1 A nerve impulse gets to the end of a sensory neuron.

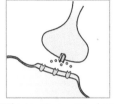

2 The sensory neuron releases the transmitter chemical into the synapse.

3 The transmitter chemical diffuses across the synapse.

4 The transmitter chemical arrives at receptor molecules on the motor neuron's membrane. Its molecules are the correct shape to bind to the receptor molecules.

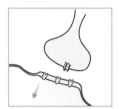

5 A nerve impulse is stimulated in the motor neuron.

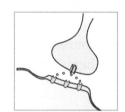

6 The chemical is absorbed back into the sensory neuron to be used again.

B6.2.14–16 How do drugs affect synapses?

Some drugs, including Ecstasy, beta blockers, and Prozac, make it more difficult for impulses to get across synapses.

Ⓗ **Serotonin** (a transmitter chemical) is released at some brain synapses. This gives a feeling of pleasure. Sensory neurons later remove the serotonin.

Ecstasy (MDMA) blocks the places that remove serotonin. So the serotonin concentration in the synapse increases. This may make Ecstasy users feel happy for a while. But Ecstasy is harmful.

B6.2.17–18 What's inside the brain?

Different regions of the brain do different jobs. Neuroscientists map the brain by:
*   studying patients with brain damage
*   electrically stimulating different parts of the brain
*   doing MRI scans.

The **cerebral cortex** is the part of the brain most closely linked to intelligence, language, memory, and **consciousness** (being aware of yourself and your surroundings).

B 6

B6.3.1–4 Can you learn reflex responses?

Animals can learn a reflex response to a new stimulus. The new stimulus (the **secondary stimulus**) becomes linked to the primary stimulus. This is **conditioning**.

Pavlov taught a dog to salivate when it heard a bell ring:
- The dog's simple reflex was to salivate when it was given food.
- Pavlov rang a bell while the dog was eating.
- After a while, the dog salivated every time it heard the bell, even if there was no food.

In this **conditioned reflex**, the stimulus (hearing the bell) became linked to food. The final response (salivating) had no direct connection to the stimulus.

Conditioned reflexes are a simple form of learning. They increase an animal's chance of survival. For example, many bitter-tasting caterpillars are brightly coloured. A bird tastes these caterpillars, and learns not to eat them. This helps the caterpillars to survive.

B6.3.5 Can you control reflexes?

Sometimes your brain consciously changes a reflex response.
- You pick up a hot object. An impulse travels to your spinal cord. Your reflex response is to drop the plate.
- But another nerve impulse travels up your spinal cord to your brain. The impulse returns down a motor neuron. This makes a muscle movement in your arm that stops the reflex response.
- You keep hold of the hot object until you can put it down safely.

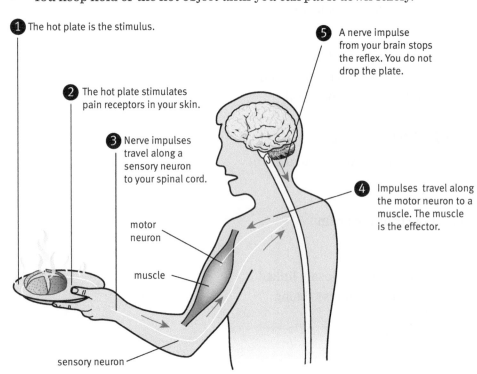

1. The hot plate is the stimulus.
2. The hot plate stimulates pain receptors in your skin.
3. Nerve impulses travel along a sensory neuron to your spinal cord.
4. Impulses travel along the motor neuron to a muscle. The muscle is the effector.
5. A nerve impulse from your brain stops the reflex. You do not drop the plate.

motor neuron

muscle

sensory neuron

6.4.1–7 How do we develop complex behaviour?

Mammals can change their behaviour as a result of new experiences. This is **learning**.

Mammal brains have billions of neurons, connected in **pathways**. Learning creates new pathways. Young animals quickly create many new pathways. Adults also make new pathways. Here's how:

- You experience something new.
- A nerve impulse travels along a particular pathway, from one neuron to another, for the first time. This makes new connections between the neurons.
- You repeat the experience.
- More impulses go along the same pathway. The connections get stronger.
- Nerve impulses travel along the pathway more easily. It is easier to respond in the way that you practised.

The variety of possible brain pathways means that animals can adapt to new situations. They have a better chance of survival.

Early humans evolved large brains, which increased their chance of survival.

Evidence suggests that children can only acquire some skills at a certain age. For example, a **feral** (wild) child cannot learn to speak if they are found after the best age for learning language skills.

B6.4.8–12 What is memory?

Memory is the storage and retrieval of information by the brain.

- **Short-term memory** lasts about 30 seconds. Scientists see this as an active **working memory**, where you can hold and process information you are thinking about now.
- **Long-term memory** is a seemingly limitless store of information that can last a lifetime.
- **Sensory memory** stores sound and visual information.

Psychologists have developed **models of memory**. All the models have limitations.

- **Multistore model** – this explains how some information is passed to the long-term memory store and how some information is lost.
- **Working memory** – you are more likely to remember something if you process it deeply. This happens if you can find patterns, or if you can organise the information.
- **Repetition** – psychologists think that repeating information moves information from the short-term to long-term memory.

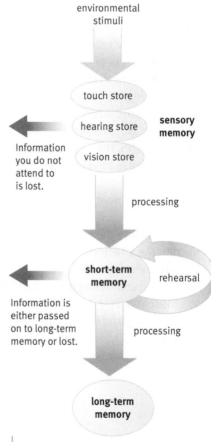

The multistore model of memory.

B6

Use extra paper to answer these questions if you need to.

1 Write **S** next to the sentences that best apply to simple animals, like woodlice. Write **C** next to the sentences that best apply to complex animals, like horses.
   a These animals rely on reflex actions for most of their behaviour. __
   b These animals can change their behaviour. __
   c The animals find it difficult to respond to new situations. __
   d These animals can learn to link a new stimulus to a reflex action. __

2 Give the names of:
   a the two parts of the central nervous system
   b two types of neurons in the peripheral nervous system.

3 Draw lines to match each 'message carrier' in the left column to two characteristics in the right column.

Message carrier	Characteristic
electrical impulse	travels quickly
	travels in the blood
hormone	brings about long-lasting changes
	brings about short-term changes

4 The stages below describe how information is passed along a simple reflex arc. They are in the wrong order. Write the letters of the stages in the correct order.
   A A receptor cell detects dust in your eye.
   B The effectors (muscles in your eyelid) blink to remove the dust.
   C In the CNS, the impulse passes to a relay neuron.
   D In the CNS, the impulse passes to a motor neuron.
   E An impulse travels along a motor neuron to the effectors.
   F A sensory neuron carries electrical impulses to your CNS.

5 Write **S** next to the sensors in the list below, and **E** next to the effectors.
   a skin cells that detect pain __
   b cells in your retina that detect light __
   c muscle cells in a baby's finger __
   d a sweat gland that releases sweat when you are nervous __

e taste buds on your tongue __
f semi-circular canals in your ear that detect movement __
g the salivary gland that releases saliva when you smell food __

6 Complete the sentences below.
   a Early humans had a better chance of survival because they evolved big b_____.
   b Your brain has billions of n_____.
   c The cerebral cortex is the part of your brain most concerned with c_____, l_____, i_____ and m_____.
   d Different areas of the cortex have different jobs. Scientists have mapped these areas by...

7 The stages below describe how new pathways develop in your brain when you learn to iceskate. They are in the wrong order. Write the letters of the stages in the correct order.
   A You ice skate for the first time.
   B More impulses go along the same pathway.
   C There is now a new neuron pathway.
   D You go ice skating again.
   E An impulse travels along a certain pathway, passing from one neuron to another, for the first time.
   F The connection between the neurons gets stronger.
   G You now find it much easier to iceskate.

8 Write **T** next to the statements that are **true**. Write corrected versions of the statements that are **false**.
   a Short-term memory is a seemingly limitless store of information.
   b You are more likely to remember information if you can find patterns in the information.
   c Repetition moves information from your long-term memory to your short-term memory.
   d The multistore model of memory states that any information you ignore is lost from your memory.
   e Your sensory memory stores only memories linked to sounds.
   f Short-term memory lasts about 30 seconds.

H 9 Explain why:
   a reflex responses are automatic and very quick
   b ecstasy increases the concentration of serotonin in synapses
   c conditioned reflexes increase an animal's chance of survival
   d mammals can adapt to new situations.

1   This question is about reflex actions.

a   Sarah is five months old. Look at the list of things that she does.

Tick the **two** actions that are newborn reflexes.

She grips a finger that is put into the palm of her hand. ☐

She stops crying when her sister sings to her. ☐

She steps when her feet touch a flat surface. ☐

She cries when her favourite toy is taken away. ☐

She goes to sleep in her pram. ☐   [2]

b   Until she was two months old, Sarah sucked anything that was put into her mouth.

Complete the sentences.

Sucking is the response to the stimulus of _____

_____

The newborn sucking reflex helped Sarah's survival by making sure she got enough _____.   [2]

c   Humans rely on reflex actions for only some of their behaviour.

Worms rely on reflex actions for most of their behaviour.

Give one advantage to worms of relying on simple reflex actions for most behaviour.

_____

_____   [1]

Total [5]

2   Describe and explain three methods that help humans to remember information.

✎ The quality of written communication will be assessed in your answer to this question.

Write your answer on separate paper or in your exercise book.

Total [6]

3   Tom and Sam investigate the effect of caffeine on reaction time.

Tom holds a metre ruler. Sam watches him.

Tom drops the ruler.

He measures the distance the ruler falls before Sam catches it.

He does the test five times, and records the results in a table.

B 6

Next, Sam drinks a caffeine drink, and Tom repeats the tests.

The results are in the table opposite.

The shorter the distance the ruler falls before Sam catches it, the quicker Sam's reaction time.

	Distance ruler falls before Sam catches it (cm)					
	Test 1	Test 2	Test 3	Test 4	Test 5	Mean
before caffeine drink	51	45	50	47	48	
after caffeine drink	30	33	32	29	35	

a **i** Complete the table by calculating the mean values for the distance the ruler falls before Sam catches it, both before and after the caffeine drink.

Record the mean values in the empty boxes, rounding each answer to the nearest whole number. [2]

ii Comment on what the investigation tells you about the effect of caffeine on reaction time.

_____

_____ [1]

iii Explain why a person's reaction cannot be instantaneous.

_____

_____ [2]

b Pippa and Kate investigate the effect of another factor on reaction time.

Their results are in the table.

	Distance ruler falls before Kate catches it (cm)					
	Test 1	Test 2	Test 3	Test 4	Test 5	Mean
in a silent room	60	62	58	59	61	60
with loud music playing	75	77	75	73	75	75

i Write a conclusion for Pippa and Kate's investigation, saying what the investigation shows.

_____

_____ [2]

ii Pippa wants to investigate the effect of alcohol on Kate's reaction time.

Describe an ethical argument **against** investigating this factor.

_____

_____ [1]

Total [8]

4 **a** Draw a line to match each part of the nervous system to its job.

Part of nervous system		Job
effector cells		control the body's response to a stimulus
receptor cells		detect a stimulus
brain and spinal cord		make changes in response to a stimulus

[2]

b Josh is crossing the road. He sees a car coming towards him.

A signal travels from his eyes to his adrenal glands.

His adrenal glands release a hormone, adrenaline.

The adrenaline helps Josh to get out of the way of the car before it hits him.

i The path taken by the nerve signal is shown in the diagram.

Use these words to finish labelling the diagram.

> **sensory neuron**
>
> **motor neuron**
>
> **central nervous system**

[3]

ii Finish the sentences. Choose the best words from this list.

Use each word once, more than once, or not at all.

> **peripheral   central**
>
> **electrical   chemical**

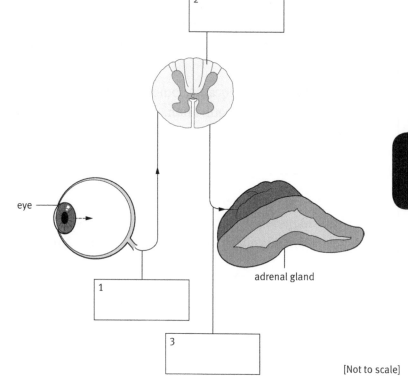

eye

adrenal gland

[Not to scale]

The signal is carried along

nerve cells by _____ impulses. The sensory

and motor neurons are part of the _____

nervous system. The brain and spinal cord form the

_____ nervous system.   [3]

Total [8]

5   Dolphins are mammals. They can learn to jump through
    hoops. Use ideas about repetition, nerve impulses, and neuron
    pathways to explain how a dolphin's brain changes as it learns
    to jump through hoops.

    _____

    _____

    _____ **[3]**

                                            Total [3]

Going for the highest grades

Ⓗ 6   Synapses are gaps between neighbouring neurons.

    a   Describe how nerve impulses cross a synapse.

        _____

        _____

        _____ **[4]**

    b   Cocaine is an illegal drug. It increases the concentration
        of serotonin in synapses. It works in a similar way to
        Ecstasy.

        i   Suggest how cocaine could cause this change of
            serotonin concentration.

            _____

            _____

            _____ **[2]**

        ii Suggest why cocaine causes an increase in the
            transmission of nerve impulses across synapses.

            _____

            _____

            _____ **[2]**

                                            Total [8]

1 Write each example from the box in an appropriate place on the diagram.

| paracetamol |
| polythene |
| saccharin (a sweetener) |
| ammonium nitrate |

food additives e.g.

_____

fertilisers e.g.

_____

Chemical synthesis provides chemicals for...

pharmaceuticals e.g.

_____

plastics e.g.

_____

pigments e.g. titanium oxide

2 The pie chart shows the percentage value of products made by the chemical industry in the UK.

Complete the sentences.

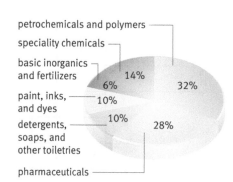

petrochemicals and polymers

speciality chemicals

basic inorganics and fertilizers

paint, inks, and dyes

detergents, soaps, and other toiletries

pharmaceuticals

14% 6% 32% 10% 10% 28%

a Chemicals used in _____ earn the most money for the British chemical industry.

b The total percentage value of paints, inks, dyes, and pharmaceuticals is _____.

c The percentage value of detergents, soaps, and other toiletries is _____% less than that of speciality chemicals.

3 For each reaction A, B, and C, decide which of the methods below you could use to measure the rate of reaction. Write the letters A, B, and C below the appropriate methods. You may choose more than one method for each reaction.

A $Mg(s) + H_2SO_4(aq) \longrightarrow MgSO_4(aq) + H_2(g)$

B $CaCO_3(s) + 2HNO_3(aq) \longrightarrow Ca(NO_3)_2(aq) + CO_2(g) + H_2O(l)$

C $Na_2S_2O_3(aq) + 2HCl(aq) \longrightarrow 2NaCl(aq) + SO_2(aq) + H_2O(l) + S(s)$

C6

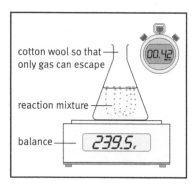

cotton wool so that only gas can escape

reaction mixture

balance

239.5.

00.42

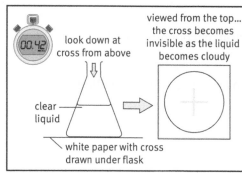

00.42

look down at cross from above

viewed from the top... the cross becomes invisible as the liquid becomes cloudy

clear liquid

white paper with cross drawn under flask

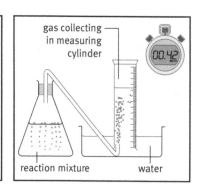

gas collecting in measuring cylinder

00.42

reaction mixture

water

4 The diagram shows apparatus for a titration.

   Use the phrases in the box to label the diagram.

   | accurately weighed | solid sample | pure water |
   | titration flask | acid or alkali | burette |

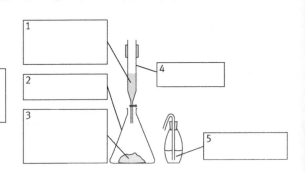

5 Solve the clues to fill in the grid.

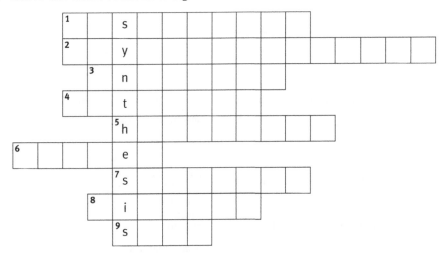

1 Use a _____ to finish drying a crystalline product of a synthesis.

2 Obtain a solid product from its solution by _____.

3 The point in a titration at which the reaction is just complete.

4 A chemical that speeds up a chemical reaction but is not used up in the process.

5 Alkaline solutions contain _____ ions.

6 Use more dilute solutions to make a reaction go _____.

7 React _____ acid with magnesium ribbon to make magnesium sulfate.

8 React nitric acid with calcium carbonate to make calcium _____.

9 A _____ is formed when an acid neutralises an alkali.

C6.1.1–2 Why is chemical synthesis important?

Chemical synthesis provides important chemicals for food additives, fertilisers, dyes, paints, and pharmaceuticals (medicines).

Bulk chemicals are made on a huge scale. They include ammonia, sodium hydroxide, sulfuric acid, and chlorine.

C6.1.7–10, C6.1.18–19 What are acids and alkalis?

An **acid** is a compound that dissolves in water to give a solution of pH less than 7. Acids produce hydrogen ions, $H^+(aq)$, in water.

Pure acidic compounds include:
* solids, for example, citric acid and tartaric acid
* liquids, for example, sulfuric acid, nitric acid, and ethanoic acid
* gases, for example, hydrogen chloride.

An **alkali** dissolves in water to give a solution of pH greater than 7. Alkalis produce hydroxide ions, $OH^-(aq)$, in water. Alkalis include potassium hydroxide, sodium hydroxide, and calcium hydroxide.

Indicators show whether a solution is acidic, alkaline, or neutral. **pH meters** also measure pH.

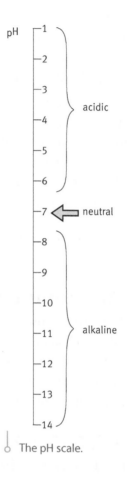

The pH scale.

C6.1.11, 16, 17, 20, 22 How do acids react?

Acids make **salts** in many of their reactions. Salts are ionic compounds that can be made from reactions of acids.

* **acid + metal $\longrightarrow$ a salt + hydrogen**
  For example:
  hydrochloric acid + calcium $\longrightarrow$ calcium chloride + hydrogen
  $$2HCl(aq) \quad + \quad Ca(s) \longrightarrow \quad CaCl_2(aq) \quad + \quad H_2(g)$$
* **acid + metal oxide $\longrightarrow$ a salt + water**
  nitric acid + magnesium oxide $\longrightarrow$ magnesium nitrate + water
  $$2HNO_3(aq) + \quad MgO(s) \quad \longrightarrow \quad Mg(NO_3)_2(aq) \quad + H_2O(l)$$
* **acid + metal carbonate $\longrightarrow$ a salt + carbon dioxide + water**
  sulfuric acid + magnesium carbonate $\longrightarrow$ magnesium sulfate + carbon dioxide + water
  $$H_2SO_4(aq) \quad + \quad MgCO_3(s) \quad \longrightarrow \quad MgSO_4(aq) \quad + \quad CO_2(g) \quad + H_2O(l)$$
* **acid + metal hydroxide $\longrightarrow$ a salt + water**
  hydrochloric acid + sodium hydroxide $\longrightarrow$ sodium chloride + water
  $$HCl(aq) \quad + \quad NaOH(aq) \quad \longrightarrow \quad NaCl(aq) \quad + H_2O(l)$$

This is a **neutralisation** reaction. Hydrogen ions from the acid react with hydroxide ions from the alkali:
$$H+(aq) + OH–(aq) \longrightarrow H_2O(l)$$

C 6

C6.4.21 How do we work out salt formulae?

Nitric acid (HNO_3) reacts with sodium hydroxide (NaOH) to make sodium nitrate. What is the formula of sodium nitrate?
- Charge on hydrogen ion = +1. So charge on nitrate ion = −1.
- Charge on hydroxide ion = −1. So charge on sodium ion = +1.

The total charge on the two ions in sodium nitrate is zero. So the formula has one Na^+ ion and one NO_3^- ion. The formula is $NaNO_3$.

C6.1.23–25 Why do energy changes matter?

Chemists need to know the energy changes in chemical reactions to minimise fuel costs and avoid accidents. Reactions can be:
- **exothermic** – they give out energy to the surroundings, making the temperature of the reaction mixture increase
- **endothermic** – they absorb energy from the surroundings, making the temperature of the reaction mixture decrease.

Energy-level diagrams show whether a reaction is exothermic or endothermic.

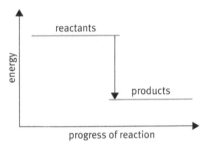
An exothermic reaction.

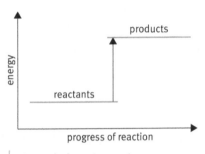
An endothermic reaction.

C6.2.5–6 What is relative atomic mass?

The **relative atomic mass** is the mass of an atom compared to the mass of a carbon atom. The relative atomic mass of carbon is 12. The relative atomic mass of helium is 4. So a carbon atom is 3 times heavier than a helium atom. The periodic table shows the relative atomic mass of every element.

C6.2.1a–f, C6.2.9–10 How can we do a chemical synthesis?

Choose the reaction to make the product

You need to make calcium chloride. You could make it by reacting hydrochloric acid with calcium *or* calcium oxide *or* calcium carbonate. Calcium carbonate is cheapest, so use the reaction:

calcium carbonate + hydrochloric acid ⟶ calcium chloride + carbon dioxide + water

Do a risk assessment

Identify hazardous chemicals, and any other hazards, and take precautions to minimise risks from these hazards.

Work out the amounts of reactants to use

Add excess calcium carbonate to dilute hydrochloric acid.
- Calculate the relative formula masses of the reactants and calcium chloride.
- Calculate the relative reacting masses of these chemicals.

- Add units to convert to reacting masses.
  $$CaCO_3(s) + 2HCl(aq) \longrightarrow CaCl_2(aq) + CO_2(g) + H_2O(l)$$
  Relative formula masses:
      100   36.5   111
  Reacting masses:
      110 g   36.5 g   111 g
- Scale reacting masses up or down to calculate amounts to use.
  To make 11.1 g of calcium chloride you need $(71 \div 10) = 7.1$ g of hydrogen chloride. This is the mass in 50 cm³ of hydrochloric acid solution of concentration 142 g/litre.
  10 g of calcium carbonate reacts exactly with 7.1 g of hydrochloric acid. You need excess, so use about 12 g.

Do the reaction in suitable apparatus in the right conditions

- Use small lumps of the solid – powder reacts too fast.
- The excess calcium carbonate does not dissolve.

Separate the product from the reaction mixture

- Use **filtration** to separate the excess solid calcium carbonate from the product (calcium chloride solution).

Purify the product

- Heat gently in an **evaporating dish** to evaporate some water.
- Leave the concentrated solution to cool and crystallise.
- Put the crystals in an oven and then a **desiccator** to dry.

Measure the yield of the product

- The **actual yield** is the mass of product you made.
- The **theoretical yield** is the maximum possible yield of calcium chloride, calculated at the start.
- You can calculate the **percentage yield** like this:

$$\text{percentage yield} = \frac{\text{actual yield}}{\text{theoretical yield}} \times 100\%$$

C6.2.1g, 6.2.3, 6.2.11 How can we check the purity of a product?

Products must be of the correct purity for their purpose.

To check the purity of solid citric acid:

- Fill a burette with sodium hydroxide solution. Make sure you know its exact concentration.
- Accurately weigh a sample of the solid citric acid. Put it in a conical flask.

C
6

- Add pure water to the solid. Stir until it dissolves.
- Add a few drops of phenolphthalein indicator. This is colourless in acid solution.
- Add sodium hydroxide solution from the burette. Stop adding it when one drop of sodium hydroxide solution makes the indicator go pink.

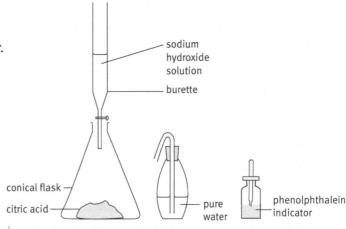

Apparatus for measuring the purity of a sample of solid citric acid.

C6.2.13–21 What are reaction rates?

The **rate of a reaction** is a measure of how quickly it happens. Chemists control reaction rates so that a reaction is not dangerously fast or uneconomically slow.

Measuring reaction rate

Methods for following reaction rate include:
- collecting a gas product and recording its volume regularly
- measuring mass decrease as a gas forms and escapes
- measuring the time for a known mass of solid to disappear
- measuring the time for a precipitate to hide a cross.

Factors affecting reaction rate

These factors affect the rate of a reaction:
- The **concentration** of reactants in solution – more concentrated solutions react faster.
- **Temperature** – increasing the temperature increases reaction rate.
- **Surface area** – 10 g of a powdered solid has a bigger surface area than 10 g of one lump of the same chemical. Increasing surface area increases the amount of contact between the solid and solution. This increases the reaction rate.
- A **catalyst** speeds up a reaction. It is not used up in the reaction.

Molecules have a greater rate of collision in a more concentrated solution.

one big lump (slow reaction)   several small lumps (faster reaction)

C6.1.3–5, 6.1.12–15, 6.2.7 Fundamental chemistry

The Module C5 Fact bank shows how to calculate relative formula mass. Modules C4 and C5 give many opportunities to practise writing word equations and interpreting symbol equations.

H The Module C4 Factbank shows how to work out formulae of ionic compounds, and charges on ions. It also includes a section on balancing equations.

Formulae for many elements, compounds, and ions are also given.

Use extra paper to answer these questions if you need to.

1 Write the names of these pure acidic compounds in a bigger copy of the table.

tartaric, ethanoic, hydrogen chloride, nitric, citric, sulfuric

Gas	Liquid	Solid

2 For the sentences below:
   • Write **acid** next to each sentence that is true for **acids**.
   • Write **alkali** next to each sentence that is true for **alkalis**.
   • Write **both** next to each sentence that is true for both **acids and alkalis**.
   a They have a pH less than 7. _____
   b They produce OH⁻ ions when they dissolve in water. _____
   c They make litmus indicator turn red. _____
   d They neutralise acids. _____
   e Wear eye protection when working with these. _____
   f Concentrated solutions of these are more dangerous than dilute solutions. _____
   g Use a pH meter to measure the pH of solutions of these. _____

3 Katie added lumps of calcium carbonate to hydrochloric acid. The calcium carbonate and hydrochloric acid reacted together. Katie did the reaction 5 more times.
Tick one column in each row to show how the reaction rate changes each time.

Change	The reaction gets ...		
	faster	slower	can't tell
a Use bigger lumps of calcium carbonate.			
b Use more concentrated acid.			
c Heat the reaction mixture.			
d Use bigger lumps of calcium carbonate and heat the mixture.			
e Add a catalyst.			

4 Write definitions of the phrases below.
   a relative atomic mass
   b exothermic reaction

5 Riana dissolved 1.5 g of impure tartaric acid in pure water. She titrated with sodium hydroxide solution. At the end point, 19.0 cm³ of alkali had been added. Use the formula below to find the percentage purity of the product.

$$\% \text{ purity} = \frac{\text{titre} \times 7.58}{\text{mass of tartaric acid}}$$

6 Fill in the empty boxes. Use the periodic table to get the data you need.

Name of chemical	Formula	Relative formula mass
nitrogen gas		
nitric acid		
	$MgSO_4$	
	KCl	
calcium chloride		
	Na_2CO_3	
calcium carbonate		

7 Do calculations to fill in the empty boxes.

Formula of product	Actual yield	Theoretical yield	Percentage yield
SrO	98 kg	104 kg	
Al_2O_3	222 g	224 g	
SF_6	68 t	73 t	

Ⓗ8 a The formula of magnesium carbonate is $MgCO_3$. Carbonate ions have a charge of -2. What is the charge on a magnesium ion?
   b The formula of aluminium oxide is Al_2O_3. The formula of an oxide ion is O^{2-}. What is the charge on an aluminium ion?

9 Fill in the empty boxes.

Name of salt	Formula of acid used to make the salt	Formula of hydroxide used to make the salt	Formula of salt
potassium chloride	HCl	KOH	
sodium sulfate	H_2SO_4	NaOH	
calcium nitrate	HNO_3	$Ca(OH)_2$	
lithium chloride	HCl	LiOH	

10 Balance the equations below. Then calculate the reacting masses for each of the substances shown in the equations.
   a $NaOH + HCl \longrightarrow NaCl + H_2O$
   b $KOH + H_2SO_4 \longrightarrow K_2SO_4 + H_2O$
   c $Mg + O_2 \longrightarrow MgO$
   d $Li + O_2 \longrightarrow Li_2O$
   e $AgNO_3 + NaCl \longrightarrow AgCl + NaNO_3$
   f $Pb(NO_3)_2 + KCl \longrightarrow PbCl_2 + KNO_3$
   g $Fe_2O_3 + C \longrightarrow CO + Fe$
   h $CaCO_3 \longrightarrow CaO + CO_2$

C6

1 Mia reacts small lumps of calcium carbonate with dilute hydrochloric acid.

   She uses the apparatus below.

   a i Complete the equation below to show:

   - the **formula** of the salt that is formed

   - the **state symbol** for each of the chemicals at room temperature.

   $2HCl$ ___ $+ CaCO_3(s) \longrightarrow$ ___ $(aq) + CO_2$ ___ $+ H_2O$ ___ [3]

   ii Mia makes 1.60 g of carbon dioxide.

   Calculate the mass of calcium carbonate that reacted to make 1.60 g of carbon dioxide. Show your working.

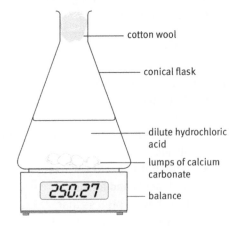

cotton wool

conical flask

dilute hydrochloric acid

lumps of calcium carbonate

250.27

balance

Mass of calcium carbonate = _____ g [2]

   b Mia records the mass of carbon dioxide produced by the reaction every minute.

   Her results are in the table below.

Time (minutes)	Mass of carbon dioxide produced since start (g)
0.0	0.00
1.0	1.10
2.0	1.40
3.0	1.56
4.0	1.60
5.0	1.60

   Calculate the rate of reaction in the first minute. Show your working.

Rate of reaction in the first minute = _____ g/min
[1]

c   Mia does the experiment four more times.

Each time she changes one of the reaction conditions.

She calculates the rate of reaction during the first minute.

Her results are in the table below.

The rate that is missing from the table is the rate you calculated in answer to part b.

Experiment	Rate of reaction during first minute (g/min)
original experiment	
W	1.10
X	2.20
Y	0.70
Z	0.50

i   Give the letter of one experiment in which Mia might have used a less concentrated acid than in the original experiment.

Give a reason for your choice.

_____ [1]

ii   Suggest two changes to the conditions of the original experiment that Mia might have made in experiment X.

_____

_____ [2]

d   An energy-level diagram for the reaction of calcium carbonate with dilute hydrochloric acid is shown opposite.

What does the energy-level diagram tell you about the reaction?

_____

_____ [2]

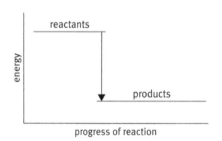

Total [11]

2   Two students investigated the claim on a carton of blackcurrant drink.

"Our blackcurrant drink has four times more vitamin C than orange juice."

The students first titrated 10.00 cm³ samples of **orange juice** with DCPIP solution. DCPIP reacts with vitamin C. The more DCPIP required, the greater the amount of vitamin C in the

C 6

drink sample. The titration results of the two students are in the tables below.

Jude

	Run 1 (rough)	Run 2	Run 3	Run 4	Run 5
Initial burette reading (cm³)	1.00	13.60	25.50	37.50	2.50
Final burette reading (cm³)	13.60	25.50	37.50	49.60	17.50
Volume of DCPIP added (cm³)	12.60				

Lucy

	Run 1 (rough)	Run 2
Initial burette reading (cm³)	2.00	14.30
Final burette reading (cm³)	14.30	26.30
Volume of DCPIP added (cm³)	12.30	12.00

a   Whose data are more likely to give a value for the volume of DCPIP required that is closest to the true value? Give a reason for your decision.

_____

_____ [1]

b   i   Calculate the volumes of DCPIP added for each run in Jude's titration. Write your answers in the table of Jude's results above.

ii   Use your answer to part to identify the outlier in Jude's results.

_____ [1]

iii   Jude decided to discard the outlier value. Suggest why.

_____ [1]

c   Use the results in Jude's table to calculate the mean volume of DCPIP that reacts with 10.00 cm³ of orange juice. Include units in your answer.

_____

_____ [1]

d   Jude then titrated 10.00 cm³ samples of the blackcurrant drink with DCPIP. The mean volume of DCPIP required was 1.50 cm³.

Do the results of Jude's titrations with orange juice and blackcurrant drink support the claim on the blackcurrant drink carton?

"Our blackcurrant drink has four times more vitamin C than orange juice."

Explain your answer.

_____

_____ [1]

Total [5]

3 a Raj wants to know the purity of a
sample of citric acid.
He does a titration to find out.
He uses this apparatus.

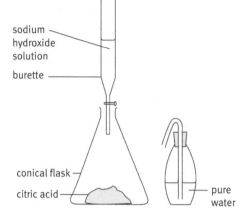

The stages below describe how Raj
does the titration.

They are in the wrong order.

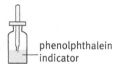

A Accurately weigh out a sample
of citric acid. Put it in the conical
flask.

B Add sodium hydroxide solution from the burette, a few
cubic centimetres at a time. Swirl after each addition.

C Add sodium hydroxide solution from the burette, drop by
drop. Swirl after each addition.

D Add a few drops of phenolphthalein indicator. This is
colourless in acid solution.

E Stop adding sodium hydroxide solution when the indicator
is permanently pink.

F Add pure water. Stir until the solid dissolves.

Fill in the boxes to show the correct order.
The first one has been done for you.

A					

[3]

b The reaction in the titration is a neutralisation reaction.

i Complete the word equation for the reaction.

citric acid + sodium hydroxide $\longrightarrow$ sodium citrate + _____

[1]

ii The reaction can be represented by an **ionic equation**.
Complete the ionic equation.

H^+ + _____ $\longrightarrow$ _____

[2]

iii Give the name of the chemical that supplied the H^+ ions.

_____ [1]

Total [7]

**C
6**

4 Two students, Grace and Nzila, make copper sulfate crystals by reacting excess copper oxide powder with dilute sulfuric acid.

Below are the word and symbol equations for the reaction.

copper oxide + sulfuric acid $\longrightarrow$ copper sulfate + water

$CuO(s) \quad + \quad H_2SO_4(aq) \longrightarrow \quad CuSO_4(aq) \quad + H_2O(l)$

The students work separately.

Grace achieves a yield of 61% for her copper sulfate crystals. Nzila's yield is 92%.

Describe the steps for making the crystals. For each step, suggest a difference in technique between the two students that might explain their different yields.

The quality of written communication will be assessed in your answer to this question.
Write your answer on separate paper or in your exercise book. **Total [6]**

> **Exam tip**
>
> If you're asked to write instructions for an experiment, jot down rough notes first to make sure you don't forget any of the stages.

⊕ Going for the highest grades

5 A company extracts mercury from its ore, mercury sulfide, by heating the ore in air.

This is the equation for the reaction.

$$HgS(s) + O_2(g) \longrightarrow SO_2(g) + Hg(l)$$

a Calculate the maximum mass of mercury that can be extracted from 233 kg of mercury sulfide.

Answer = _____ kg [2]

b In 2011, the company produced 1005 kg of mercury.

What mass of sulfur dioxide gas did the company produce as a by-product?

Answer = _____ kg [2]

c Sulfur dioxide can be used to make sulfuric acid.

This is a simplified summary of the process:

$$SO_2 + \tfrac{1}{2}O_2 \longrightarrow SO_3$$
$$SO_3 + H_2O \longrightarrow H_2SO_4$$

What is the maximum mass of sulfuric acid that the company could make from the sulfur dioxide produced in b?

Answer = _____ kg [2]

Total [6]

1 The diagram compares three types of ionising radiation.

For each bold pair of words or phrases, highlight the word or phrase that is correct.

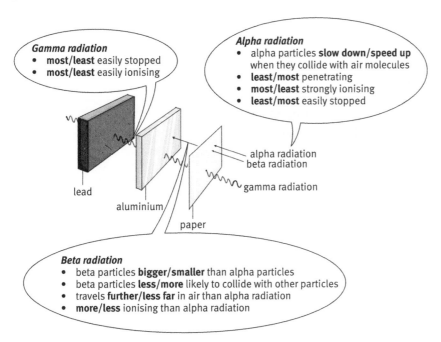

Gamma radiation
- **most/least** easily stopped
- **most/least** easily ionising

Alpha radiation
- alpha particles **slow down/speed up** when they collide with air molecules
- **least/most** penetrating
- **most/least** strongly ionising
- **least/most** easily stopped

lead
aluminium
paper

alpha radiation
beta radiation
gamma radiation

Beta radiation
- beta particles **bigger/smaller** than alpha particles
- beta particles **less/more** likely to collide with other particles
- travels **further/less far** in air than alpha radiation
- **more/less** ionising than alpha radiation

2 The table shows how different sources of radiation contribute to the average radiation dose in the UK.

Write the name of each radiation source by the correct section of the pie chart.

Radiation source	Average radiation dose in the UK (mSv)
radon gas from the ground	1.25
food and drink	0.24
cosmic rays	0.30
medical	0.38
gamma rays from the ground and buildings	0.33
fallout	0.0005
occupational	0.0005

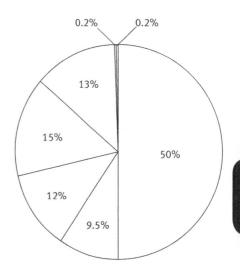

3 Fill in the gaps to complete the labels on this diagram of an atom.

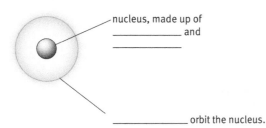

nucleus, made up of
_____ and
_____

_____ orbit the nucleus.

4 Annotate the diagram to describe and explain what happened when Geiger and Marsden fired alpha particles at a piece of gold foil in a vacuum.

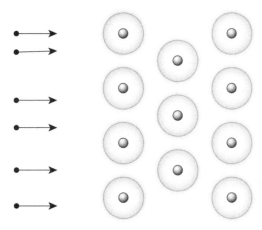

H 5 The diagrams show the number of protons and neutrons in six atoms.

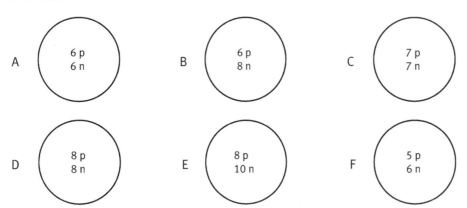

A 6 p 6 n

B 6 p 8 n

C 7 p 7 n

D 8 p 8 n

E 8 p 10 n

F 5 p 6 n

a Give the letters of two pairs of atoms of the same element.
_____

b Give the letter of the atom that has the fewest total number of particles in its nucleus. _____

c Give the letter of the atom that has the greatest total number of particles in its nucleus. _____

d Give the letters of two atoms that have the same total number of particles in their nuclei. _____

P6.1.1, P6.1.9 What are radioactive materials?

Radioactive materials give out (emit) ionising radiation all the time. You cannot change the behaviour of a radioactive material – it emits radiation whatever its state (solid, liquid, gas) and whether or not it has taken part in a chemical reaction.

P6.1.10–11 What types of ionising radiation are there?

Type of radiation	Penetration properties	Ⓗ What is it?
alpha (α)	absorbed by paper, clothing, skin, and a few cm of air	a positively charged particle made up of two protons and two neutrons
beta (β)	penetrate paper; absorbed by a thin sheet of metal	an electron
gamma (γ)	absorbed only by thick sheets of dense materials (e.g. lead) or several metres of concrete	a high-energy electromagnetic wave

P6.1.3–6 What's in an atom?

Three scientists (Geiger, Marsden, and Rutherford) fired alpha particles at thin gold foil in a vacuum. Most alpha particles passed through the foil. A few of the positively charged alpha particles were reflected backwards.

The scientists concluded that a gold atom has a small, massive, positive region at its centre – its **nucleus**.

We now know that every atom has a tiny core, or **nucleus**. The nucleus is surrounded by **electrons**.

The nucleus is made up of **protons** and **neutrons**. Protons are positively charged. Neutrons have no charge.

Ⓗ Protons and neutrons are held together by a strong force. This balances the repulsive electrostatic force between the protons.

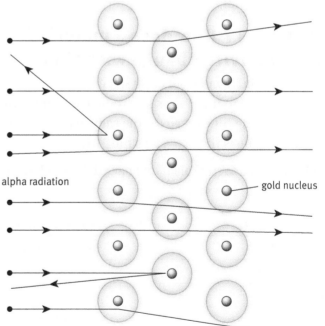

alpha radiation

gold nucleus

P 6

If two hydrogen nuclei are brought closely together, they may join to make a helium nucleus. The process releases energy. It is called **nuclear fusion**.

Ⓗ P6.1.7–8 and P6.1.12–13 What makes a substance radioactive?

Every atom of a certain element has the same number of protons. Different atoms of this element may have different numbers of neutrons. Atoms of the same element that have different numbers of neutrons are called **isotopes**. For example:

Name of isotope	Number of protons	Number of neutrons	Is this isotope radioactive?
carbon-12	6	6	no
carbon-14	6	8	yes

The nucleus of carbon-12 is stable. It is not radioactive.

The nucleus of carbon-14 is unstable. It decays to make a stable nucleus of another element, nitrogen. As it decays, it emits beta radiation. You can summarise this reaction in a **nuclear equation**:

$$^{14}_{6}\text{C} \longrightarrow {}^{14}_{7}\text{N} + {}^{0}_{-1}\beta$$

Other elements have atoms with unstable nuclei, for example, radium-226. When a radium-226 atom decays, it emits alpha radiation to make a radon-222 atom. This is the decay product.

$$^{226}_{88}\text{Ra} \longrightarrow {}^{222}_{86}\text{Rn} + {}^{4}_{2}\alpha$$

When an atom decays, energy is released. Einstein's equation calculates how much energy is released for a given loss of mass.

energy = change in mass × (speed of light)²

or $E = mc^2$

> **Exam tip**
>
> Practise writing nuclear equations.

P6.1.14–17 How does a material's radioactivity change with time?

As a radioactive material decays, it contains fewer atoms with unstable nuclei. It becomes less radioactive and emits less radiation. The time taken for the radioactivity to fall to half its original value is the material's **half-life**.

Different radioactive elements have different half-lives:

Radioactive element	Half-life
plutonium-242	380 thousand years
carbon-14	5.6 thousand years
strontium-90	28 years
iodine-131	8 days
lawrencium-257	8 seconds

The shorter the half-life, the greater the activity for the same amount of material.

The graph shows the decay curve for iodine-131. After 8 days, 50% (half) of the original sample remains, and the activity is half its original value.

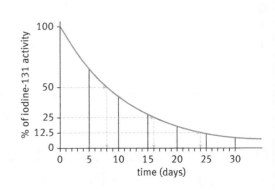

P6.1.2, P6.2.1–2, P6.2.6–7 What are the risks from radioactive sources?

We are exposed to **background radiation** all the time. There are many radioactive substances in the environment. These contribute to background radiation.

If ionising radiation reaches you from a source outside your body, you are being **irradiated**. If a radioactive material gets onto your skin or clothes, or inside your body, you are **contaminated**. You will be exposed to the radiation as long as the material stays there.

When ionising radiation hits atoms and molecules, it may break them into charged particles, called **ions**.

Ⓗ The ions formed may then take part in other reactions.

The ions damage living cells:
- Larger amounts of radiation may kill cells.
- Smaller amounts may damage a cell's DNA, causing cancer.

P6.2.3 How is ionising radiation useful?

Ionising radiation has many uses:
- To treat cancer by **radiotherapy**.

Ⓗ The ionising radiation damages cancerous cells and they stop growing.

- To sterilise surgical instruments, and herbs and spices.

Ⓗ The ionising radiation kills bacteria on the instruments or food.

- To help diagnose disease by acting as a tracer in the body.

Ⓗ For example, radioactive krypton-81m gas shows doctors how gases move in diseased lungs.

P6.2.4, P6.2. 9 What are the risks of handling radioactive materials?

The more ionising radiation a person is exposed to, the greater the risk to health. **Radiation dose** measures the possible harm to your body. It takes account of the amount and type of radiation. Its units are sieverts (Sv).

Hospital radiographers and nuclear power station workers are exposed to radioactive sources. Their exposure is monitored.

P6.2.10–13 How do nuclear power stations generate electricity?

Radioactive materials release energy from changes in the nucleus. They can be used as **nuclear fuels**.

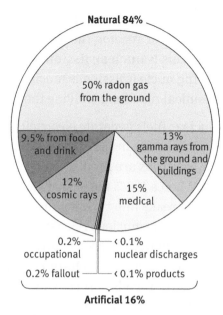

The UK average annual dose is 2.5mSv.

This pie chart shows the contribution of different sources to the average background radiation dose in the UK. Source HSE.

P 6

Uranium-235 is a nuclear fuel. Its nucleus is large and unstable. In a nuclear reactor, the nucleus breaks into two parts of similar size. This is **nuclear fission**. The amount of energy released during nuclear fission is much greater than that released in a chemical reaction involving the same mass of material.

(H) Nuclear fuels generate electricity like this:
- **Fuel rods** in the nuclear reactor contain uranium-235 (U-235).
- Neutrons are fired at the U-235.
- When a U-235 nucleus absorbs a neutron, it becomes unstable. It breaks into two smaller parts of similar size. At the same time, the nucleus releases more neutrons. Energy is released.
- The newly released neutrons hit more U-235 nuclei. Fission happens again. A **chain reaction** has started.
- **Control rods** absorb neutrons. They are moved into or out of the reactor to control the reaction rate.
- A fluid **coolant** is pumped through the reactor. The fuel rods heat up the coolant.
- The coolant heats up water, which becomes steam.
- The steam turns turbines, which turn a generator.

P6.2.8, P6.2.14–15 What happens to nuclear waste?

Nuclear power stations produce dangerous radioactive waste.

Scientists use half-lives to work out when nuclear waste will become safe. Elements that have long half-lives remain hazardous for many thousands of years; those with short half-lives quickly become less dangerous.

Type of waste	Example	How it is disposed of
low level	used protective clothing	packed in drums and dumped in a lined landfill site
intermediate level	materials that have been inside reactors – may remain highly radioactive for many years	mixed with concrete and stored in stainless steel containers
high level	concentrated radioactive material from spent fuel rods	decays fast and releases energy rapidly, so needs cooling; in the UK, stored in a pool of water at Sellafield

Use extra paper to answer these questions if you need to.

1 In the list below, tick the statements that describe ways in which ionising radiation is used in the UK.
  a to treat cancer ☐
  b as a tracer in the body ☐
  c to sterilise spices ☐
  d to generate electricity ☐

2 Write **T** next to the statements that are true. Write corrected versions of the statements that are false.
  a Radioactive materials emit radiation all the time.
  b Atoms of carbon-14 are radioactive. If a carbon-14 atom joins to oxygen atoms to make carbon dioxide, the carbon dioxide will not be radioactive.
  c Solid caesium chloride that is made with caesium-137 is radioactive. It remains radioactive when it dissolves in water.
  d Radiation dose is measured in half-lives.
  e Radiation dose is based on the amount and type of radiation a person is exposed to.
  f Hydrogen nuclei can join together to make helium nuclei. This process is called nuclear fission.
  g The energy released in a nuclear reaction is much less than the energy released in a chemical reaction involving a similar mass of material.

3 Draw lines to match each word or phrase to its definition.

Word or phrase	Definition
irradiation	having a radioactive substance inside your body
contamination	a measure of the possible harm to your body caused by radiation
radiation dose	being exposed to radiation from a source outside your body

4 List two groups of people whose exposure to radiation is carefully monitored.

5 Doctors use radioactive krypton-81m gas to help diagnose lung diseases.
  a Krypton-81m has a half-life of 13 seconds. Explain why it would be a problem if the half-life was much longer than this.
  b A sample of krypton-81m has an activity of 4000 Bq. After how long will its activity be reduced to 1000 Bq?
  c Krypton-81m emits gamma rays. Suggest two safety precautions hospital staff must take when using this gas.

Ⓗ 6 Complete the sentences below.
  In the nucleus of an atom, protons and _____ are held together by a _____ force. This balances the repulsive _____ force between the protons.
  A radioactive atom has an _____ nucleus. The nucleus _____ to become more stable, emitting energetic _____ in the process.

7 The table shows the half-lives of some radioactive uranium isotopes.

Element	Half-life
uranium-222	1.4 milliseconds
uranium-228	9 minutes
uranium-231	4 days
uranium-232	69 years

  a A scientist has some uranium-228. Its relative activity is 100. After what time period will its relative activity be 50?
  b A scientist has some uranium-231. After what time period will its activity be one quarter that of its original activity?
  c A scientist has some uranium-232. Its relative activity is 100. After what time period will its relative activity be 12.5?

8 Give the numbers of protons and neutrons in each of the isotopes of uranium below.
  a $^{239}_{92}U$ **b** $^{225}_{92}U$ **c** $^{217}_{92}U$

9 A nuclear power station releases 66×10^9 J of energy to provide a family of four with their electricity needs for one year. Calculate the mass of fuel that must be lost to provide this energy.
  Use the equation $m = \dfrac{E}{c^2}$.
  The value of c is 3×10^8 m/s.

10 Describe the purpose of each of the following in a nuclear power station.
  a fuel rod   **b** control rod   **c** coolant

11 Complete the nuclear equations by giving the proton number and atomic mass/mass number for each of the atoms, alpha particles, and beta particles.
  a $_{92}U^{239} \longrightarrow Np + _{-1}\beta^{0}$
  b $^{14}C \longrightarrow {}_{7}N + \beta$
  c $^{235}U \longrightarrow {}_{90}Th + {}_{2}\alpha^{4}$
  d $_{83}Bi^{209} \longrightarrow {}_{81}Tl^{205} + \underline{\quad\quad}$
  e $_{86}Rn \longrightarrow {}^{215}Po + \alpha$

P 6

111

1 Read the article about treating cancer with radioactive materials.

> Arthur has a cancer tumour deep inside his body. His doctors will use radiotherapy to treat it. Arthur's doctors and radiotherapists plan the treatment carefully. They tattoo his skin to show exactly where to direct the radiation, and calculate the dose of radiation Arthur must receive.
>
> Arthur gets his treatment in a lead-lined room. When everything is ready, the radiotherapist leaves the room. Once outside, she switches on the treatment machine. Gamma rays enter Arthur's body for a few minutes. During the treatment, the radiotherapist watches Arthur on closed-circuit television. They can talk to each other over an intercom.
>
> Arthur goes to hospital for treatment every weekday for five weeks. On each visit, the gamma radiation enters his body at a different angle.

a   i   What type of material emits the radiation that enters Arthur's body?

_____

    ii Why does the radiotherapist use gamma radiation, and not alpha or beta radiation?

_____

_____ [2]

b   i   What does gamma radiation do to cancer cells?

_____

    ii Why is it important to direct the radiation exactly at the cancer tumour?

_____

_____ [2]

c   i   Why are the walls of the treatment room lined with lead?

_____

    ii Suggest why the radiotherapist leaves the room while Arthur is receiving his treatment.

_____

_____ [2]

Total [6]

2 Caesium-137 (Cs-137) emits beta particles. It is used to treat some cancers.

The graph shows how the activity of this radioactive source changes over time.

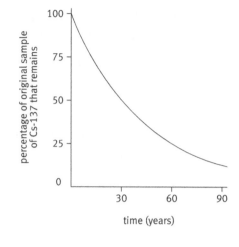

a Read the statements below.
Put ticks in the boxes next to each true statement.

The activity of the Cs-137 source decreases over time. ☐

All radioactive elements have a half-life of between 10 and 50 years. ☐

The half-life of Cs-137 is 30 years. ☐

The longer the half-life of a radioactive source, the more quickly it becomes safe. ☐

Beta radiation is absorbed only by thick sheets of lead or concrete. ☐ [2]

b A sample of caesium chloride contains 10 g of caesium-137.

Calculate the mass of caesium-137 that will remain after 120 years.

_____

_____ [2]

c Caesium-137 decays to barium-137. Barium-137 is not radioactive.

Complete the following sentences.

Use the words in the box.

| negative | unstable | stable | neutral |

The nucleus of a caesium-137 atom is _____.

It decays and emits beta radiation. This makes barium-137,

which has a nucleus that is _____. [2]

Total [6]

P 6

3 a Nuclear power stations generate electricity.
      The stages in this process are shown below.

   A These neutrons hit more uranium-235 nuclei. Fission
         happens again. A chain reaction has started.

   B The steam turns a turbine.

   C Energy from the fission reaction is transferred as heat
         to a coolant, such as water or carbon dioxide.

   D The unstable nucleus splits into two smaller parts of
         about the same size. This is fission. At the same time,
         the nucleus releases more neutrons.

   E Neutrons are fired at fuel rods.

   F When a neutron hits the nucleus of a uranium-235
         atom, the nucleus becomes unstable.

   G The hot coolant heats up water in a boiler to make steam.

      The stages are in the wrong order.

      Write a letter in each box to show the correct order.

E	F					B

                                                              [1]

   b Complete the following sentences.
      Choose from the words in the box.

barium	**protons**	**electrons**	**boron**
bismuth	**neutrons**	**rate**	

      Control rods control the _____ of fission

      reactions when they are lowered into or raised out of the

      nuclear reactor. They contain _____ to absorb

      _____.   [3]

   c Nuclear power stations produce radioactive waste.
      Draw straight lines to match each **type of waste** to its
      disposal method.

Type of waste	Disposal method
low level	Mix it with concrete and store it in stainless steel containers.
medium level	Pack it in drums. Dump it in a lined landfill site.
high level	Store in a pool of water.

                                                              [2]

                                               Total [6]

4 Scientists asked parents in five US states to send in baby teeth from their children. The scientists measured the amounts of strontium-90 in about 2000 of these teeth. In 2003, scientists published a scientific paper about their findings.

The bar charts show some of their results.

a Look at the bar charts.

   i Describe the trend shown by the bar charts.

     _____

     _____ [2]

   ii Suggest why the graph for Pennsylvania includes no data for people born between 1982 and 1985.

     _____ [1]

b The scientists suggested that the levels of strontium-90 were caused by an increase in the amount of electricity generated in nuclear power stations from 1986 onwards.

Do the data in the bar charts support this conclusion? Give a reason for your decision.

_____

_____ [1]

c The scientists looked at their data again.
They found that teeth from children living within 64 km of a nuclear power station had up to 54% more strontium-90 in them than teeth from children living further from nuclear power stations.

Does this finding make the conclusion in part more or less likely to be correct? Give a reason for your decision.

_____

_____ [1]

Total [5]

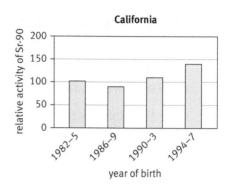

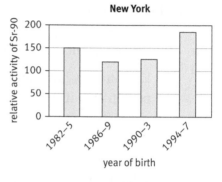

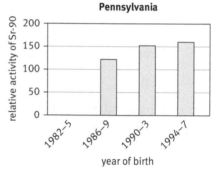

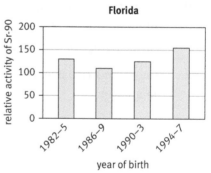

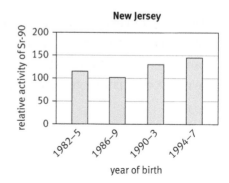

**P
6**

Going for the highest grades

⊕ 5

> In March 2011, an earthquake damaged a nuclear power station in Fukushima, Japan.
>
> Over the next few months, scientists analysed 100 soil samples taken from distances of up to 80 km from the power station.
>
> Levels of radioactive plutonium-238 were higher than normal in six of the soil samples, including in a sample taken from a village 45 km from the power station.
>
> Plutonium-238 from the soil can enter the body if it is breathed in, or eaten with food.
>
> It is then deposited in the lungs and bones.

a Plutonium-238 decays by emitting alpha particles.

    i Explain why plutonium-238 may be a health risk to a person only if it gets inside their body.

    _____

    _____ [2]

    ii What is an alpha particle made up of?

    _____ [1]

b Complete the equation below for the decay of plutonium-238.

$$^{238}_{94}\text{Pu} \longrightarrow \quad \text{U} \quad + \quad \alpha$$ [2]

c A decay curve from Pu-238 is shown below.
Use the decay curve to estimate the half-life of Pu-238.

_____ [2]

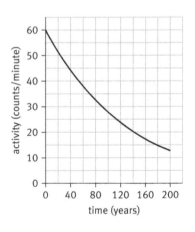

d Radioactive plutonium-239 was found in some soil samples. Calculate the number of protons and neutrons in an atom of this isotope of plutonium.

You will need to use data from part **a** to help you work out the answer.

_____ [1]

Total [8]

⊕ 6 Describe and explain how ionising radiation is used in hospitals.
🖊 The quality of written communication will be assessed in your answer to this question.
Write your answer on separate paper or in your exercise book.

Total [6]

Data: their importance and limitations
IaS1.1–1.5 (part)

1

2

3

4

5

6

7

Overall, the scientists claim that their results are *repeatable*. The same scientists, using the same equipment and sending the neutrinos on the same journey, got similar results many, many times.

The scientists spent months doing checks, and didn't find any errors.

8

The scientists must have calculated the *mean* time for all those journeys. The mean gives the best estimate of its true value.

9

What about the *range*? Isn't that important?

10

Yes, the range is the maximum and minimum value of a variable.

For the set of repeated time measurements, the true value probably lies within the range of the journey times measured.

11 (H)

Now the scientists want to know if their results are *reproducible*. Different scientists based in Japan and the USA will do similar investigations. Will their neutrinos travel faster than light?

12 (H)

If different scientists using different equipment get similar results, the measurements are reproducible.

And we can be more confident that the explanation is correct... Neutrinos travel faster than light.

IaS 1.5 (part), IaS1.6

1

Our generator is better than yours.
Our results say it all... The induced voltage from our generator is higher.

2

I don't think so. Show me your data.

This is the data. You can see our mean, and the range.

3

Hmm. That all looks fine...

.... No it's not – there's an outlier. That value is well outside the range of your other repeats. If you included that in your average, no wonder your value for the voltage is so high.

4

Actually, we checked that value. The next time we got a value inside our range.

So we decided to discard the outlier.

5

So you see, our generator really does generate electricity with a higher voltage.

I'm going to ask the teacher to check. Miss Smith – over here, please!

6

H

Well, your means are different. Your ranges do not overlap.

So I'm confident there is a real difference in the voltage you each generated.

Congratulations to the higher-voltage team!

Data: their importance and limitations

1 Draw lines to match each word or phrase to its definition.

Word or phrase	Definition
A true value	**1** The value obtained by adding up several values for the measurement of a quantity, and dividing by the number of values.
B repeatable	**2** A measurement is _____ if the same investigator obtains similar results when making the measurement again in the same conditions.
C reproducible	**3** A measurement is _____ if different investigators obtain similar results when making the measurement with different equipment.
D mean	**4** The size of a quantity that would be obtained in an ideal measurement.
E range	**5** The closeness of a measured value to the true value.
F outlier	**6** The maximum and minimum values obtained for the measurement of a variable.
G accuracy	**7** A value in a set of results that lies well outside the range of the others in a set of repeats.

2 Each table below is designed to collect a set of data about the rate of reaction of magnesium with hydrochloric acid.

Give the letter or letters of the best table or tables in each case. You are collecting data to compare how the rate of the reaction varies with:

a   acid concentration   ___ and ___

b   temperature   ___ or ___ or ___ or ___

c   surface area of magnesium.   ___ and ___ and ___

A   acid concentration = 1.0 mol/dm³; one 6 cm long piece of magnesium ribbon

Temperature (°C)	Time to collect 100 cm³ gas (s)
0	
20	
40	
60	
80	

B   acid concentration = 2.0 mol/dm³; one 6 cm long piece of magnesium ribbon

Temperature (°C)	Time to collect 100 cm³ gas (s)
0	
20	
40	
60	
80	

C   acid concentration = 1.0 mol/dm³; magnesium powder

Temperature (°C)	Time to collect 100 cm³ gas (s)
0	
20	
40	
60	
80	

D   acid concentration = 1.0 mol/dm³; six 1 cm long pieces of magnesium ribbon

Temperature (°C)	Time to collect 100 cm³ gas (s)
0	
20	
40	
60	
80	

3 Clarise had a piece of tin. She wanted to know its melting point.

She took five readings. Her results are in the table.

Test number	Melting point (°C)
1	227
2	229
3	236
4	230
5	230

a Calculate the mean value of the melting point measurements.

_____

b Why is it better to take several melting point measurements, rather than just one?

Put ticks in the **two** correct boxes.

to make it a fair test ☐

to be more confident the result is close to the true value ☐

to check the data are repeatable ☐

to check there is nothing wrong with the thermometer ☐

c Clarise looks up the melting point of tin in a data book. It is 232 °C.

Suggest why the data book value is different from Clarise's mean value.

_____

Data: their importance and limitations

1 Ben needs to know the concentration of a solution of sodium hydroxide.

He places exactly 25.0 cm³ of sodium hydroxide solution in a conical flask.

He adds a few drops of indicator.

He titrates the mixture with hydrochloric acid.

His results are in the table below.

	Volume of hydrochloric acid required (cm³)			
	Rough	Run 1	Run 2	Run 3
Initial burette reading (cm³)	0.3	12.0	23.5	35.0
Final burette reading (cm³)	12.3	23.5	34.9	46.3
Volume of acid added (cm³)	12.0	11.5	11.4	

a i Suggest why Ben repeated the titration several times.

_____ [1]

ii Suggest why the measurements of the volume of hydrochloric acid required have different values.

_____ [1]

b Calculate the volume of acid added in run 3.

answer = _____ cm³ [1]

c i Identify the outlier in the set of data in the table.

_____ [1]

ii The student decided to discard the outlier. Suggest why.

_____ [1]

d Estimate the range within which the true value for the volume of acid required probably lies.

_____ [1]

e Calculate the mean volume of acid needed to exactly neutralise the sodium hydroxide solution.

answer = _____ cm³ [2]

Total [8]

2   Tillie wants to find out the resistance of a coil of wire.

She sets up the circuit opposite.

Tillie records values for voltage and current.

She adjusts the variable resistor, and records the voltage and current again.

She repeats until she has collected the data in the table below.

Voltage (V)	Current (A)	Resistance (Ω)
1.5	0.060	
3.0	0.115	26.0
4.5	0.188	24.0
6.0	0.240	25.0
7.5	0.234	

a   Use the equation $R = V/I$ to calculate the missing values for resistance.

Write your answers in the table above.   [1]

b   i   Identify the outlier from all the values for R in the table.

_____ [1]

ii   Suggest what Tillie should do about the outlier you have identified.

_____ [1]

c   Charlie does the same investigation as Tillie.

She uses the same coil of wire, but a different ammeter, voltmeter, and variable resistor.

Charlie's results are in the table below.

Voltage (V)	Current (A)	Resistance (Ω)
3.0	0.115	26
3.5	0.121	29
4.0	0.154	26
4.5	0.196	23
5.0	0.192	26

i   Compare Tillie's and Charlie's data sets.

Which data set has the bigger range for the voltage values?

Explain how you decided.

_____

_____ [1]

ii Estimate the true value of the resistance of the coil from Charlie's data.

Answer = _____ Ω [2]

d Tillie calculates from her data that the mean value for the resistance of the coil was 25.0 Ω.

Use Tillie's and Charlie's data sets to explain whether or not you think the true value of the resistance of the coil changed when measured with a different set of equipment.

_____

_____

_____

_____ [3]

Total [9]

3 Lilia is investigating how temperature affects the rate of photosynthesis.

She sets up the apparatus opposite.

She draws a table for her results.

water ⎯⎯⎯
pondweed ⎯⎯
paper clip ⎯⎯
'weight'

Temperature (ºC)	Number of bubbles produced in 1 minute
10	
20	
30	
40	
50	

a Lilia collects a set of results.

Describe how she could find out if the results are repeatable.

_____

_____ [2]

b Lilia's teacher asks if her results are reproducible. Suggest how Lilia could find out.

_____

_____ [2]

Total [4]

Cause–effect explanations
IaS2.1, IaS2.2

1

Mr Webster told us to investigate factors that affect the rate of photosynthesis of pondweed. Where shall we start?

2

*Well, the **outcome** is the rate of photosynthesis. We can measure this by counting bubbles.*

3

*What **factors** might affect the outcome?*

What's a factor?

*It's the same as an **input variable**. And outcome means the **outcome variable**.*

4

So the factors that might affect the outcome could be light intensity, carbon dioxide concentration, pH, temperature...

Let's investigate the effect of changing temperature. I think that the higher the temperature, the faster the rate of photosynthesis.

5

*OK. So to make it a **fair test**, we need to control all the other factors. Otherwise the design of our investigation will be flawed.*

6

Yes. We keep light intensity, carbon dioxide concentration, and pH constant. We change just one factor – temperature.

IaS2.3, 4, 6, 7

1

And now for some good news.

New research shows that chocolate may be good for you. German scientists claim that eating just one square of chocolate every week lowers blood pressure.

2

That's not right.

Everyone knows that chocolate is bad for you.

What about its high energy content?

Let's see what the scientists really said.

3

OK. I've found the scientists' research paper...

They recruited 44 volunteers with slightly high blood pressure.

Half the volunteers ate one square of dark chocolate every week for 18 weeks. The others ate one square of white chocolate each week.

4

The scientists measured the volunteers' blood pressure regularly.

There was no change in blood pressure for the white chocolate group.

For the dark chocolate group, the blood pressure decreased gradually over the 18 weeks. Look at this graph...

5

Yes, there's a correlation – regularly eating a little dark chocolate reduces blood pressure.

The outcome (reduced blood pressure) occurs when a certain factor (eating dark chocolate) is present.

Blood pressure stayed the same in people who did not eat dark chocolate.

6

But the correlation doesn't mean that the factor **caused** the outcome. There could be some other reason for the reduced blood pressure.

Like maybe the dark chocolate group started doing exercise every week, or something.

7

Exactly. Let's find out more about the samples.

Well, there were 44 volunteers altogether. That's a reasonable size, but I'd be more confident in the conclusions if the sample size had been even bigger.

8

The investigation was a randomised, controlled trial. That means that the volunteers were randomly put into either the white or the dark chocolate group.

2

9

All factors were the same, except the type of chocolate.

Neither group did more exercise than the other, so this couldn't have caused the blood pressure change.

10

In random groups, other factors are equally likely in both groups.

The average age, weight, and waist size for each group were almost the same in each group – the scientists checked.

11

So there seems to be good evidence that the factor caused the outcome.

(H) But I'd be happier if there was a **mechanism** that linked the dark chocolate to the lowered blood pressure.

12

(H) There is! The dark chocolate volunteers had extra nitrogen monoxide in their blood.

Scientists think that flavanol compounds in dark chocolate made the amount of nitrogen monoxide increase.

Nitrogen monoxide helps make blood vessels wider. And this can reduce blood pressure.

Cause–effect explanations

1 For each graph, chart, and table below, describe the correlation between the factor and the outcome.

A

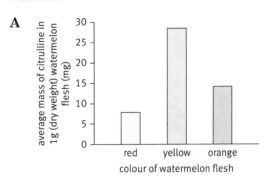

Correlation _____

_____

B

Correlation _____

_____

C

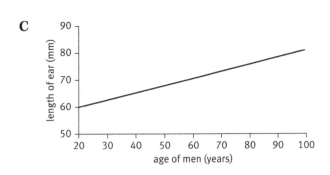

Correlation _____

_____

D

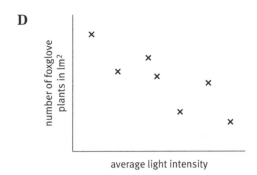

Correlation _____

_____

E

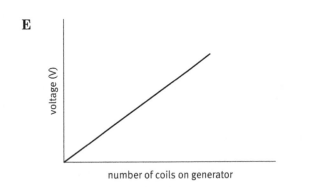

Correlation _____

_____

F

Temperature (°C)	Time to collect 100 cm³ gas in the reaction of magnesium with dilute hydrochloric acid (s)
10	120
20	60
30	31
40	16
50	7

Correlation _____

_____

2 Use the clues to fill in the grid.

1   A correlation between a factor and an outcome does not necessarily mean that there is a c... link.

2   Scientists often think about processes in terms of factors that may affect an o...

3   An input variable is also called a f...

4   In an investigation, if you control all factors that may affect an outcome except the factor you are investigating, you are doing a f... test.

5   When there is evidence that a factor is correlated with an outcome, scientists will only accept that the factor causes the outcome if they can think of a sensible m... to link the factor and outcome.

6   If you are investigating the effect of a factor on an outcome, and you do not control other factors, your investigation design is f...

7   Smoking increases your c... of getting lung cancer.

8   To investigate the claim that a factor increases the chance of an outcome, scientists may compare samples that are m... on as many other factors as possible.

9   If an outcome variable i... as a factor increases, there is a correlation between the factor and the outcome variable.

10 When investigating whether mobile phone use increased the chance of cancer, scientists compared r... samples so that other factors were equally likely in both samples.

11 If you are investigating the effect of the number of coils on generator voltage, you must c... other factors such as speed of turning and whether or not there is an iron core.

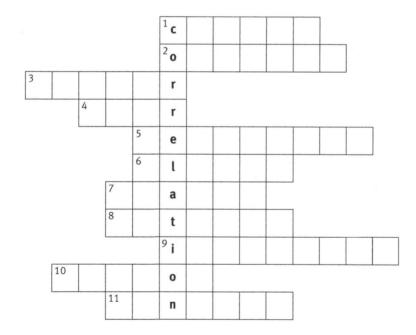

Cause–effect explanations

1 A scientist plans to investigate the effect of carbon dioxide concentration on the flavour of strawberries.

A strawberry has an intense flavour if it contains a relatively high mass of ester compounds.

The scientist grows three groups of strawberries. He adds different amounts of extra carbon dioxide to the air around two of the groups.

Each group of strawberries receives the same amount of water and is grown at the same temperature.

When the strawberries are ripe, the scientist picks them. He measures the masses of ester compounds in the strawberries of each group.

a Identify the outcome variables.

_____ [1]

b i Identify two factors (input variables) that the scientist controls.

_____ [1]

ii Explain why he controls these factors.

_____ [1]

c The table gives some results from the investigation.

Concentration of carbon dioxide in air (ppm)	Concentration of ester compound A in strawberries (ng/g)	Concentration of ester compound B in strawberries (ng/g)	Concentration of ester compound C in strawberries (ng/g)
350	651	531	53
650	815	637	54
950	963	715	53

i Describe two correlations shown by the data in the table.

_____

_____

_____ [2]

ii Four students discuss the results in the table.

Tim The correlations show that the factor causes the outcomes.

Kezi The factor might cause the outcomes, but we cannot be sure.

2

Sahira   The factor and the outcomes might both be
caused by some other factor.

Ashfaq   There is no correlation between the factor
and one of the outcomes. This shows that the
factor cannot cause the other outcomes.

Give the names of the two students whose statements
are correct.

_____ and _____   [2]

d   The scientist suggested *how* extra carbon dioxide gas in
the air may help strawberry plants to synthesise greater
amounts of ester compounds.

Explain why the scientist's suggestion may make other
scientists more willing to accept that the factor causes the
outcomes shown in the table in part **c**.

_____

_____   [1]

Total [8]

2   A group of scientists investigated the effect of taking aspirin
on the chance of getting bowel cancer.

The scientists asked people with Lynch syndrome to help
them with their research. People with Lynch syndrome are
more likely to get bowel cancer than other people because
their bodies struggle to detect and repair damaged DNA.

a   Write an O next to the **two** statements that are part of
the outcome.

Write an F next to each of the **two** statements that are
factors that may affect the outcome.

Of the people who took aspirin, 10 got cancer.   __

For 2 years, 258 people took aspirin every day.   __

For 2 years, 250 people took aspirin placebo
tablets (tablets that look like aspirin but have
no aspirin in them) every day.   __

Of the people who took aspirin placebo tablets,
23 got cancer.   __   [2]

b   Use the statements in part **a** to help you answer this question.

Tick the boxes next to all the statements below that are true.

There is a correlation between the factors and
the outcome.   ☐

Taking aspirin reduces the chance of getting bowel cancer. ☐

Taking aspirin increases the chance of getting bowel cancer. ☐

Taking aspirin means a person will not get bowel cancer. ☐ [2]

c Suggest why the groups of people in the study (aspirin or placebo) were chosen randomly.

_____

_____ [1]

d The scientists suggested a mechanism to explain how aspirin prevents bowel cancer. They think that aspirin may kill stem cells in the bowel that cannot repair damaged DNA.

Tick the box next to the two statements below that are true.

The suggested mechanism proves that taking aspirin causes a reduced chance of bowel cancer. ☐

The suggested mechanism increases confidence that taking aspirin causes a reduced chance of bowel cancer. ☐

The suggested mechanism decreases confidence that taking aspirin causes a reduced chance of bowel cancer. ☐

It is possible that the decreased chance of getting cancer after taking aspirin for 2 years is caused by some other factor. ☐ [2]

e Another group of scientists researched the effects of aspirin on several different cancers.

They studied 12 500 patients for 20 years. They found that the risk of cancer death was reduced by 20% for patients taking aspirin.

i Suggest two factors that might affect the risk of getting cancer, other than taking aspirin.

_____

_____ [2]

ii Identify one aspect of the study that increases confidence in its conclusions.

_____ [1]

Total [10]

Ideas about science

Developing scientific explanations

IaS3.1–4

In the 1770s, French chemists Antoine Lavoisier and Maria-Anne Lavoisier were at work in their laboratory.

13

I think so. But now we need to test the explanation further.

Can we use it to make predictions about new situations?

14

Let's heat phosphorus in a closed container of air.

I predict that the phosphorus will burn, and join with oxygen from the air, to make a new substance.

The volume of air will decrease by about one fifth because phosphorus will remove oxygen from it.

15

Your prediction was right, Antoine.

Now let me make another prediction to test the explanation.

If we heat some phosphorus in pure oxygen, and some in air, I predict that the burning will be faster in oxygen than in air.

16

Our predictions were right, Antoine. The burning reaction was much faster in oxygen. And, when we heated phosphorus in air, the volume of air decreased by one-fifth.

Wonderful. Our observations agree with our predictions. Now I'm even more confident in our explanation.

17

It still doesn't prove the explanation is correct, though, does it...

18

True, Maria-Anne. All we can do is make more predictions and collect more data.

The more they agree, the more convincing our explanation.

Developing scientific explanations

1   Write **T** next to the statements that are true and **F** next to the
    statements that are false.

    a   Scientific explanations simply summarise data.   ___

    b   If the data agree with an explanation, the explanation
    must be correct.   ___

    c   Developing a scientific explanation requires creative
    thought.   ___

    d   A scientific explanation must account for most, or
    all, of the data already known.   ___

    e   An explanation should always explain a range of
    phenomena that scientists didn't know were linked.   ___

    f   Scientists test explanations by comparing predictions
    based on them with data from observations or
    experiments.   ___

    g   If an observation agrees with a prediction that is
    based on an explanation, it proves that the explanation
    is correct.   ___

    h   If an observation does not agree with a prediction
    that is based on an explanation, it decreases confidence
    in the explanation.   ___

    i   If an observation does not agree with a prediction that
    is based on an explanation, then the observation must
    be wrong.   ___

    j   If an observation does not agree with a prediction that
    is based on an explanation, then the explanation must
    be wrong.   ___

Now write corrected versions of the **six** false statements on the
lines below.

_____

_____

_____

_____

_____

_____

_____

2 The statements below describe how a group of scientists tested a hypothesis about the size of a part of the brain in London taxi drivers.

Write the letter of each statement in a box on the flow chart. There is one letter for each box.

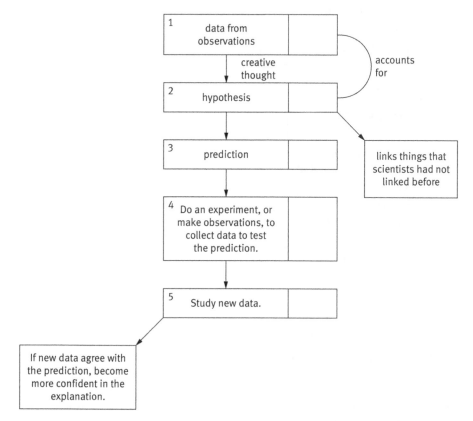

3

A   London taxi drivers have an excellent knowledge of all the street names in a 280-km² area of London.

B   We did MRI scans of 16 taxi drivers' brains, and of 50 other people's brains.

C   The back of the hippocampus part of the brain was bigger in taxi drivers than in other people.

D   The part of the brain that deals with navigation might be bigger in taxi drivers than in other people.

E   If we the measure different brain parts in taxi drivers, and compare them to those of other people, there will be size differences in the part of the brain that deals with navigation.

Developing scientific explanations

1 In the 1930s, scientists investigated the effects of bombarding uranium with neutrons.

   a Some of the statements below report **data** collected by the scientists, and one is a possible **explanation**.
      Write a **D** next to each of the three statements that are data.
      Write an **E** next to the one statement that is an explanation.

Statement	D or E
1 On bombarding uranium with neutrons, Enrico Fermi observed that at least four radioactive substances were produced.	
2 Hahn and Strassmann bombarded uranium with neutrons. At least three substances were formed that had chemical properties similar to barium.	
3 Hahn and Strassmann could not separate the substances with properties similar to barium from barium itself.	
4 Isotopes of barium are formed when uranium is bombarded with neutrons.	

[2]

   b Scientists Lise Meitner and Otto Frisch read about the work described in the table above. They came up with a new explanation:

      The uranium nucleus is unstable. When bombarded with neutrons, it divides itself into two nuclei of roughly equal size.

      Suggest why Lise and Otto must have used creative thinking to help them develop this explanation.

      _____

      _____ [1]

   c Lise and Otto used their explanation to make a prediction:

      The nuclei formed when a uranium nucleus breaks down will be unstable. These nuclei will decay to form lighter atoms.

      Later observations showed that the prediction was correct.

      Tick the boxes next to the **two** statements that are true.

      The fact that the prediction is correct proves the explanation is correct. ☐

      The fact that the prediction is correct increases confidence in the explanation. ☐

If the prediction were wrong, we would be less confident in the explanation. ☐

If the prediction were wrong, we would be sure the explanation was wrong. ☐

[2]

d Lise and Otto explained that when a uranium nucleus decays, some of its mass is converted into energy.

Describe an observation that would support this explanation.

_____

_____ [1]

Total [6]

3

2 In the 1630s, scientist Galileo investigated acceleration.

He set up the apparatus below.

He measured the times for the ball to roll down different sections of the slope.

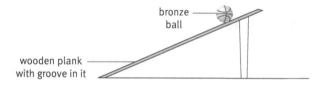

a The **statements** describe what Galileo did.

The **flow chart** shows how science explanations develop.

Write the letter of each statement in an empty box on the flow chart. Some boxes need more than one letter.

Statements

A He measured the time for the ball to roll down the whole length of the slope.

B He measured the time for the ball to roll down half the length of the slope.

C He measured the time for the ball to roll down a quarter the length of the slope.

D He calculated the acceleration of the ball for each of its journeys.

E The acceleration of the ball is the same, no matter what distance it travels.

F He thought that if he rolled the ball down a steeper slope, the acceleration of the ball would be the same, no matter what distance it travelled.

G   He measured the times for the ball to roll down different lengths of a steeper slope.

Flow chart

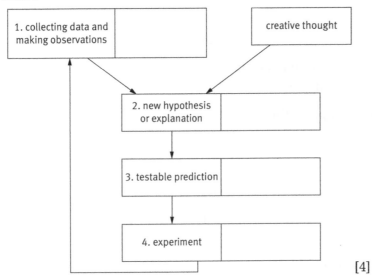

[4]

b   Galileo made the groove in the apparatus as smooth as possible. Suggest why.

_____ [1]

c   Galileo repeated his measurements many, many times. Suggest why.

_____ [1]

d   Galileo came up with another hypothesis:

The steeper the slope, the greater the acceleration of the ball.

  i   Describe how he might have tested this hypothesis.

  _____

  _____ [2]

  ii   If the hypothesis was correct, what would his results have shown?

  _____

  _____ [2]

Total [10]

The scientific community

IaS4.1–2

Reporting scientific claims in journals and at conferences gives other scientists opportunities to critically evaluate their claims... and to build on their work.

1

1829. Johann Döbereiner publishes his Law of Triads in a German journal...

The three elements sulfur, selenium, and tellurium have similar properties. The atomic mass of selenium is the average of the atomic weights of the other two elements. I will call this group a triad. There are other triads, too.

2

Other scientists evaluate Döbereiner's ideas...

His law works well for lithium, sodium, and potassium. And for chlorine, bromine, and iodine.

But some similar elements can't be grouped into triads – he said this himself... so the law doesn't always work.

We can't be confident in this claim. Other scientists need more time to evaluate it.

3

1860. Stanislao Cannizzaro presents his ideas at the First International Chemical Congress in Germany.

Here is a table of atomic masses. It is based on measurements of the weights and volumes of gases.

4

His evidence is good. His claims make sense.

I'll take a table of atomic weights. It will help with my future research.

4

IaS4.2

5

1864. John Newlands speaks about his Law of Octaves at a London Chemical Society meeting.

I have arranged all 56 known elements in order of atomic mass. There is a pattern. Every eighth element has similar properties.

6

Why have you grouped copper with lithium, sodium, and potassium? Copper has very different properties.

Why arrange elements like a musical scale? You might as well have ordered them alphabetically!

This is such a new idea. It has not been evaluated by others. We cannot accept it.

7

1869. Dmitri Mendeleev creates the periodic table.

I arranged the elements in order of atomic mass, more or less. Elements with similar properties are grouped together.

I've left gaps for elements that have not yet been discovered.

8

1875. Paul-Emile Lecoq de Boisbaudran makes a discovery.

I've found one of Mendeleev's missing elements. I've called it gallium.

This evidence makes me more confident in Mendeleev's claims.

9

1879. Lars Nilson discovers another missing element.

I've found the element between calcium and titanium. Its name is scandium.

I am very confident that Mendeleev's ideas are correct.

1

Scientists have found that juice from harlequin ladybirds destroys disease-causing bacteria.

A chemical in the juice also stops the growth of a parasite that causes malaria.

2

Interesting. Maybe this is something our research group could study. Could we **reproduce** their findings?

3

Here's their paper. It's published in a **peer-reviewed** scientific journal. So other scientists must be happy with their methods, results, and claims.

The scientists separated harmonine from ladybird juice. They purified the compound and made solutions. Then they tested the solutions against bacteria and malaria parasites. The paper describes exactly what they did.

4

Did they repeat the tests?

Yes. And they **replicated** their own findings.

4

5

Have other scientists done similar work? Does the paper say?

Before them, another research group found that harmonine was toxic to tumour cells in humans. But no-one has done exactly the same research.

6

Let's find out more. It would be great if we could reproduce their findings.

Yes. Like they say, harmonine could lead to new antibiotics, and maybe new malaria medicines.

The scientific community

1   The statements below describe some of the steps by which scientists may accept a new scientific claim or explanation.

Write each statement in a sensible place on the flow chart below.

A   Many other scientists read the paper. Some may try to reproduce its findings.

B   A small number of other scientists read the paper to check the methods and claims, and to spot any mistakes.

C   He makes a claim or creates a new explanation.

D   The scientist makes corrections to his paper.

E   He repeats the investigation to check that he can replicate his own findings.

F   Other scientists are sceptical about the new claim or explanation.

G   The paper is published in a scientific journal, in print and online.

H   Other scientists are more likely to accept the new claim or explanation.

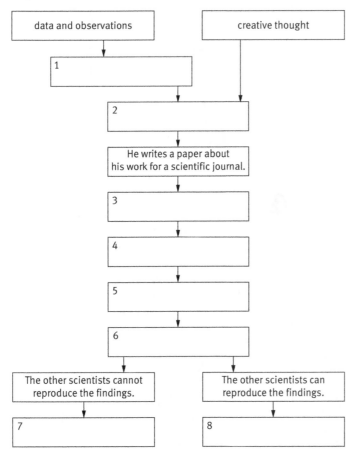

2 Draw a line to link two words or phrases on the circle.
Write a sentence on the line saying how the two words
are connected.

Repeat for as many pairs as you can.

new scientific claim

peer review   replicate

report   scientific community

unexpected findings   reproduce

scientific journal   critical evaluation

established scientific claim   scientific conference

sceptical

The scientific community

1 Between 1996 and 2001 scientists asked 1 million women to help with their health research as part of the Million Women Study.

The women wrote down their height, weight, and how much they exercised. Over the next few years, about 2500 of the women broke (fractured) their hips.

The scientists wanted to find out if there were correlations between:

- exercise and hip fracture risk
- body mass index (BMI) and hip fracture risk.

a Before starting their research, the scientists read about other scientists' research on hip fracture risks.

Put ticks next to the **two** best reasons for doing this.

Reason	Tick (✓)
to plan how to find out if the other scientists' work is reproducible	
to repeat exactly what other scientists have done	
to find as many mistakes as possible in the other scientists' investigations	
to find out what is already known about the effects of exercise and BMI on hip fracture risk	

[2]

b The Million Women Study scientists found that women who exercise are less likely to break their hips than women who do not exercise.

Other scientists made similar claims in earlier research.

Explain why the Million Women Study research increases confidence in the claims of the scientists who did the earlier research.

_____

_____ [1]

c The Million Women Study scientists wrote a paper about hip fracture risks for a scientific journal.

Before the paper was published, it was peer reviewed.

Outline the process of peer review.

_____

_____

_____ [2]

d Why might the scientists tell TV and radio journalists about their work?

Put a tick next to the **one** best reason for doing this.

Reason	Tick (✓)
so that other scientists can speak about their work at a scientific conference	
to let women know that exercising can reduce their risk of hip fractures	
so that other scientists can evaluate the quality of the explanation	
so that other scientists can try to reproduce their findings	

[1]

Total [6]

4

2 When Mendeleev created the periodic table, he left gaps for elements that had not yet been discovered.

By 1900, nearly all the gaps had been filled.

But two elements were still missing – those under manganese with atomic numbers of 43 and 75.

a In 1909, Japanese scientist Masataka Ogawa extracted a tiny amount of an unknown chemical from a mineral.

He claimed he had found element 43, and called it nipponium.

He published his findings in a scientific journal.

i Give two reasons for publishing reports in scientific journals.

_____

_____ [2]

ii A second scientist tried to reproduce the findings of Masataka Ogawa. He could not extract the new element from the mineral.

How might the second scientist's result have influenced other scientists? Tick the **two** best answers.

The result made other scientists less likely to accept Masataka Ogawa's claim. ☐

The results show that Masataka Ogawa definitely did not find a new element. ☐

The results made other scientists more likely to accept Masataka Ogawa's claim. ☐

The results made other scientists more likely to question Masataka Ogawa's claim. ☐ [2]

b   Read the article about the discovery of the element rhenium.

> In the early 1920s Ida Tacke and William Noddack extracted 1 g of a new chemical from 660 kg of an ore. The scientists thought it might be the missing element of atomic number 75.
>
> The scientists asked another scientist, Otto Berg, to look at the spectrum of the new chemical. He found some new lines in the spectrum. He explained that the new lines were from the new element.
>
> Ida Tacke announced the discovery of the new element at a conference in 1925.

i   Suggest why Ida Tacke and William Noddack asked Otto Berg to look at the spectrum of the new chemical before telling other scientists about it at the conference.

_____

_____

_____

_____ [2]

ii In 1925 Ida Tacke and William Noddack also announced that they had discovered missing element 43.

At the time, other scientists could not reproduce their findings. They thought that Ida and William were wrong.

In 1999 another scientist repeated the work of Ida and William, and obtained a similar result.

How might the result of the 1999 scientist influence other scientists?

Tick the **one** best answer.

The result would make other scientists less likely to accept Ida and William's claim. ☐

The results show that Ida and William definitely did not find a new element. ☐

The results would make other scientists more likely to accept Ida and William's claim. ☐

The results would make other scientists more likely to question Ida and William's claim. ☐ [1]

Total [7]

Ideas about science

Risk
laS5.1–5

1

I get chest pains when I walk up the stairs, Doctor. I'm worried about my heart.

We need to do some tests. One option is a thallium scan.

2

Thallium scan? What's that?

We inject radioactive thallium-201 into your vein. It travels in your blood to your heart muscle.

Heart tissue with a good blood flow emits more gamma rays than heart tissue with a poor blood flow. A camera detects the gamma rays.

3

Radioactive thallium? That sounds scary. Is it worth the risk?

Well, everything we do carries a risk of accident or harm. You need to weigh up the risks and benefits.

4

So what are the benefits?

The benefits are clear. The scan shows how blood flows in your heart arteries. It detects any blockages, too.
It helps us decide what treatment you need.

5

You do have radioactive thallium in your body. That's why we don't recommend the scan for pregnant women. The gamma radiation could harm a fetus.

The radiation slightly increases the chance of getting a fatal cancer. The extra risk is between 1 in 10 000 and 1 in 1000.

And the risks?

6

You say there's an extra cancer risk? I know the chances are tiny, but the consequences are huge. I'm not ready to die.

I understand your worry. But your chest pains show there could be a bigger risk of dying from heart disease.

5

7

Can I be sure that the risks from this scan are as low as possible?

We use only a little radiation. It's like having a few X-rays, or a few years of normal background radiation.

8

I guess there are there rules about radiation levels for these scans.

You're right. We must use as little radiation as possible to do the job.

9

Would I be contaminated forever?

Thallium-201 has a half-life of 73 hours. Its activity is one quarter of its original value in just over a week. Thallium might come out when you go to the loo, too.

10

Isn't this another risk? What can I do about it?

You need to flush twice, and wash your hands properly. That will reduce the risk to you and others.

11

I don't know what to do. Are you saying I must have the scan?

Of course not. It's up to you.

12

It's a hard decision. The consequences could be long-lasting, if I get cancer. But it is my choice... OK. I'll have the scan.

Good decision. I really believe that the benefits outweigh the risks.

IaS5.1–5

Risk

1 Below are eight answers. Make up one question for each answer.

a The chance of it occurring in a large sample over a given period of time.

_____

b The chance of it happening and the consequences if it did.

_____

c Take account of both its risks and benefits.

_____

d If they have chosen to do it.

_____

e Because they are more familiar with riding a bike.

_____

f Actions that may have long-term effects.

_____

H **g** Perceived risk.

_____

h They may overestimate the risk.

_____

2 Read the information in the box.

> Nuclear power stations rely on uranium fuel. Much uranium is mined in the form of uranium oxide, U_3O_8. The world's biggest producers of uranium are Kazakhstan, Canada, and Australia.
>
> There are health risks linked to mining. Uranium ore emits radon gas, which increases the chance of lung cancer. Today, strict regulations mean that modern mines have high standards of ventilation. Poor safety procedures in some countries may lead to air, water, and soil becoming contaminated by radioactive substances.

Make up a dialogue on the next page to get across six important points about risk.

Use the information in the box above, and the phrases on the next page.

- size of a risk
- the chance of it happening and the consequences if it did
- take account of both risks and benefits
- people more willing to accept risks that...
- acceptable risk
- perceived risk
- statistically measured (estimated) risk

1 Pete lives near a nuclear power station.
He is offered a job in the office at the power station.
He needs to decide whether or not to accept the job.

a The annual risk of a nuclear power station worker developing cancer from exposure to radiation is 0.1%. This is 40 times greater than for a member of the public.

Different people have different opinions about Pete's increased cancer risk.

Person	Opinion
Government energy minister	The calculated risk of his getting cancer is small, but if it happened the consequences would be terrible.
Pete	Nuclear power stations provide electricity for many people. This is worth the small extra cancer risk to power station workers.
Jake (Pete's son)	The extra cancer risk is significant, but there are few jobs in the area and the pay is good.

Draw lines to match each opinion to the person most likely to have the opinion. [2]

b In nuclear power stations, precautions are taken to reduce the risks to workers. Identify one of these precautions.

_____ [1]

c If there is a leak of radioactive iodine from a UK nuclear power station, children and pregnant women living nearby may be given potassium iodide tablets. The tablets help to prevent thyroid cancer.

Suggest why the tablets are given only to those living closest to the power station, not to everyone in the UK.

_____ [1]

d Kara is Pete's wife. She thinks that UK nuclear power stations should be closed down. She says:

> They should build more nuclear power stations in France. Then the UK could get all its electricity from these power stations. We already import some electricity from France. There is a cable under the sea linking the two countries.

Discuss the risks and benefits of Kara's idea, and identify how different groups of people would be affected by it.

_____

_____

_____

_____ [3]

Total [7]

2 Barbara and Tom live in the USA. They are discussing risk.

Tom The risk of nuclear power station workers getting cancer as a result of radiation exposure is less than the risk of aeroplane pilots getting cancer radiation exposure.

Job	Typical radiation dose (mSv/year)
nuclear power station worker	2.4
pilot who does not fly over the Arctic	5
pilot who regularly flies over the Arctic	9

Barbara That's not right. I go on aeroplanes all the time. But I would never visit a nuclear power station – think of all that invisible radiation! Nuclear workers must be at greater risk from cancer.

a   Who is correct, Tom or Barbara?

Use data from the table to support your answer.

_____

_____ [2]

b   Suggest two reasons for Barbara's opinion.

_____

_____

_____ [2]

Total [4]

5

3 Multiple sclerosis (MS) is a disease that damages nerves of the central nervous system. People with MS may suffer pain, stiffness, trembling, and exhaustion.

Some people with MS say that smoking cannabis makes them feel better. The boxes below describe some scientific research about cannabis and MS.

Box A	Box B	Box C
Mice with MS symptoms were injected with cannabis extract. Their stiffness and trembling decreased compared to a control group.	160 people with MS were given either a cannabis extract spray or a placebo spray. Afterwards, muscle stiffness was significantly less in the cannabis spray group.	112 people with MS who smoked cannabis filled in a questionnaire. 97% of the people said that cannabis reduced their muscle stiffness.

Box D	Box E	Box F
Cannabis can produce severe anxiety and panic. The more that is smoked, the worse the anxiety and panic.	Small amounts of cannabis cause slowed reaction times, poor coordination, and short-term memory problems.	Nine pilots smoked either a joint of cannabis or a placebo. 24 hours later they did a test in a flight simulator. The cannabis pilots made more mistakes than the placebo pilots.

a   Use the evidence in the boxes to discuss the benefits and
    risks of smoking cannabis to a person with MS.

    _____

    _____

    _____

    _____

    _____

    _____ [4]

b   In the UK, smoking cannabis is illegal.

    Suggest why some people think that it should be legal for
    people with MS to smoke cannabis.

    _____

    _____ [1]

c   Read the opinions below about people with MS smoking
    cannabis.

    Verity

    If I drive after smoking cannabis, and then crash my car,
    people could be killed.

    Will

    I am 21. If I smoke cannabis, I am twice as likely to suffer
    from hallucinations and frightening thoughts than if I
    don't smoke cannabis.

    Xena

    If I smoke cannabis regularly, and then stop, I might
    become aggressive and hurt someone.

    Yasmin

    When smoking cannabis, my heart rate could double
    compared to normal.

    i   Give the name or names of the person or people who
         are talking about the chance of a risk occurring.

         _____ [1]

    ii   Give the name or names of the person or people who
         mention the consequences of a risk.

         _____ [1]

                                          Total [7]

Making decisions about science and technology
IaS6.1–2

1

Don't buy a new phone. You don't need it. You've only had the old one a year.

New phones cost the Earth – and lives.

2

What do you mean? I couldn't live without my phone.

And they don't just benefit people in rich countries. My uncle in Tanzania says his mobile phone has changed his life. His business makes much more money now.

3

Of course. Mobile phones are a perfect example of a science-based technology improving the quality of life.

But there are costs too.

4

Costs? What costs? How can a phone cause harm?

Mobile phones store charge in capacitors, made from tantalum metal. Tantalum is extracted from a mineral called coltan. Miners in the Democratic Republic of Congo find coltan in streams. It's worth a lot of money.

5

So that's another benefit.

True. But there are impacts on the environment. And they're not good. Mining companies have cut down forests to make it easier to find and transport coltan. The forests are home to mountain gorillas. What will happen to this rare species if they destroy more forests?

6

But can't scientists be part of the solution? Maybe they can work out how to rebuild the gorilla population. Perhaps they could develop better ways of recycling tantalum from phones.

Maybe. But for now, weigh the costs against the benefits. And don't buy that phone you don't need.

IaS6.1, IaS6.3–4

1

Germany will shut down all its nuclear power stations by 2022. The government made the decision following earthquake damage to Japan's Fukushima nuclear power station in 2011.

2

I can see that people living near nuclear power stations might be pleased. They might be worried about leaks of radioactive substances, or of ionising radiation.

3

Yes, and what about radioactive waste? What if something goes wrong during its transport or storage, or if people steal it to make nuclear weapons? The costs to humans and the environment could be huge.

4

But nuclear power does have its benefits. It supplies electricity all the time – without depending on the weather, or the supply of fossil fuels.

You need to compare the costs and benefits to different groups of people.

5

There are very strict regulations about nuclear power. Waste must be carefully checked and accounted for. Nuclear workers are monitored all the time.

I think these rules reduce the risk of harm.

6

Going back to Germany, who made the decision? Is this something science can decide?

I think not. Scientists can advise about technical issues, and risk. But the decision involves values. It's up to society to judge the importance of different issues, and then to use these ideas to decide.

me... to the top right

IaS6.5–6

1

Look at this. Scientists have been giving Prozac to young mice. Then they put them in water and forced them to swim.

That can't be ethical. It's not right to treat animals like that.

2

Do you think that drugs should never be tested on animals?

Yes. It is always ethically wrong. It shouldn't be allowed... even if people benefit from the tests in the end.

3

I disagree. In my opinion, it depends on why the scientists did the investigation.

If there is a chance that lots of people might benefit, I see no ethical problem in a few mice suffering.

What were the scientists investigating?

4

They wanted to find out about the effect of Prozac on children and teenagers.

Prozac can be given to young people with severe depression. But some of them have side-effects, like feeling more anxious, or even suicidal.

The scientists wanted to find out more about these side-effects, and investigate whether they were long term.

5

Thanks. This is important research. The findings could help many people. In my view, this makes the suffering of the mice ethically acceptable.

Anyway, there are rules about how to treat research animals. I'm sure the scientists obeyed them.

6

I disagree. Experimenting on animals is always wrong, whatever the consequences.

6

Making decisions about science and technology

1 A company wants to open a new bauxite mine in Jamaica.

Aluminium metal is extracted from bauxite ore.

Different people have different opinions about the mine.

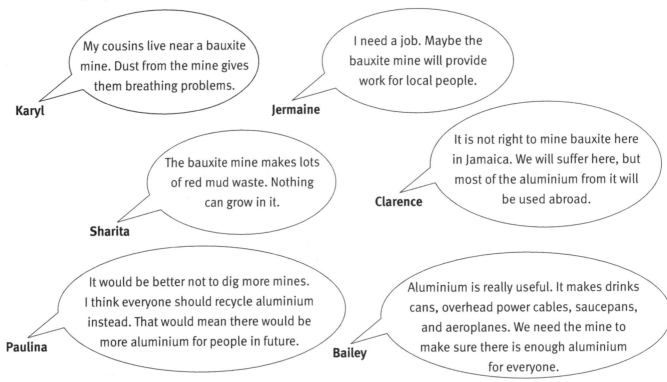

Karyl: My cousins live near a bauxite mine. Dust from the mine gives them breathing problems.

Jermaine: I need a job. Maybe the bauxite mine will provide work for local people.

Sharita: The bauxite mine makes lots of red mud waste. Nothing can grow in it.

Clarence: It is not right to mine bauxite here in Jamaica. We will suffer here, but most of the aluminium from it will be used abroad.

Paulina: It would be better not to dig more mines. I think everyone should recycle aluminium instead. That would mean there would be more aluminium for people in future.

Bailey: Aluminium is really useful. It makes drinks cans, overhead power cables, saucepans, and aeroplanes. We need the mine to make sure there is enough aluminium for everyone.

a   Write the names of the people above in the correct box in the table below.

Each name may be used once, more than once, or not at all.

You can write one or more names in each box.

A person or people who identify...	Name or names
...an impact on the environment.	
...an issue that science cannot solve.	
...issues that could be investigated scientifically.	
... an ethical issue.	
...an unintended impact on the environment.	
...an issue linked to sustainability.	

b Some friends are discussing whether it is better to extract aluminium from bauxite ore, or whether it is better to recycle the metal.

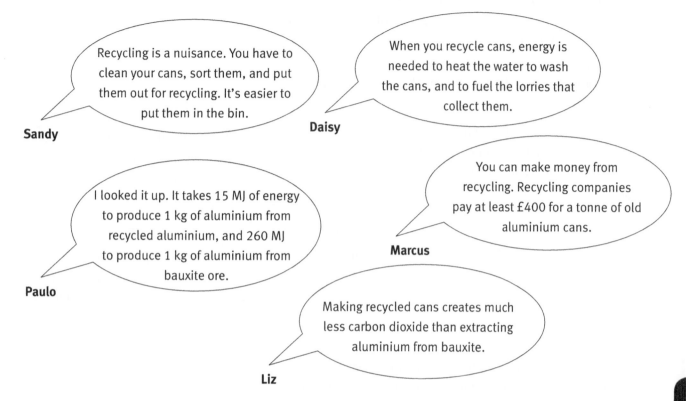

Recycling is a nuisance. You have to clean your cans, sort them, and put them out for recycling. It's easier to put them in the bin.

Sandy

When you recycle cans, energy is needed to heat the water to wash the cans, and to fuel the lorries that collect them.

Daisy

I looked it up. It takes 15 MJ of energy to produce 1 kg of aluminium from recycled aluminium, and 260 MJ to produce 1 kg of aluminium from bauxite ore.

Paulo

You can make money from recycling. Recycling companies pay at least £400 for a tonne of old aluminium cans.

Marcus

Making recycled cans creates much less carbon dioxide than extracting aluminium from bauxite.

Liz

i Use the data and opinions above and on the previous page to help you fill in the grid below.

6

	Benefits	Drawbacks
Extracting aluminium from bauxite ore		
Recycling aluminium		

ii Use the table to write a paragraph to compare the benefits and drawbacks of extracting aluminium from bauxite ore compared to recycling aluminium.

Identify which method you think is better, and give reasons for your choice.

_____

_____

_____

_____

Making decisions about science and technology

1   Graphite is a mineral. It is made up of carbon atoms.
    A European company wants to reopen an old graphite mine in
    Mozambique, Africa.

    Some people give their opinions about re-opening the mine.
    Use the opinions to help you answer the questions below.

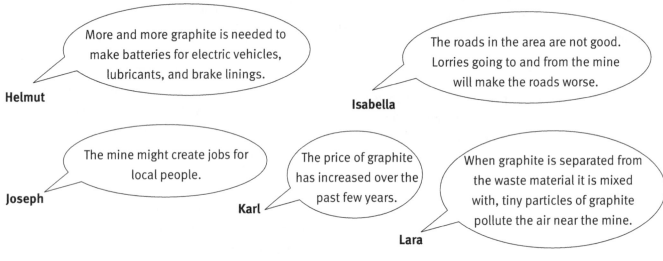

Helmut — More and more graphite is needed to make batteries for electric vehicles, lubricants, and brake linings.

Isabella — The roads in the area are not good. Lorries going to and from the mine will make the roads worse.

Joseph — The mine might create jobs for local people.

Karl — The price of graphite has increased over the past few years.

Lara — When graphite is separated from the waste material it is mixed with, tiny particles of graphite pollute the air near the mine.

   a   Identify two groups of people who might benefit from
       the mine, and suggest one way in which each group
       might benefit.

       _____

       _____ [2]

   b   Identify two problems that might be caused if the mine
       re-opens.

       _____

       _____ [2]

   c   People in Mozambique have some questions about the
       benefits and problems of reopening the mine.

       Which of the questions below could be answered using a
       scientific approach?

       Tick the correct boxes.

       What mass of graphite is in 1 tonne of rock
       from the mine?   ☐

       How much money would the mining
       company make?   ☐

       Is the graphite of good enough quality to
       make batteries?   ☐

       How does graphite dust affect health?   ☐

       Overall, would opening the mine benefit
       local people?   ☐   [2]

d   In the UK, the law states that people working with graphite must not be exposed to more than 10 mg/m³ of graphite dust on average, over 8 hours.

  i   Suggest why there is a law to limit how much graphite dust people can be exposed to.

  _____

  _____ [1]

  ii   Suggest what data scientists collected to help the government decide on the legal limit for graphite dust exposure.

  _____

  _____ [1]

  Total [8]

2   Read the article in the box.

> **British cancer chief to investigate breast cancer screening**
>
> The Government's cancer chief has set up an inquiry to investigate the advantages and disadvantages of breast cancer screening. Currently, women over 50 are offered breast cancer screening every three years. More than 80% of breast cancer cases are diagnosed in women aged 50–69. A review of scientific research in 2002 found that breast cancer screening in Sweden reduced the number of breast cancer deaths by 21%.
>
> But in 2011 other scientists found that breast cancer screening leads to unnecessary treatment. Some cancers get better by themselves, for example. Some cancer treatments, including surgery, can have bad side-effects. There is also a tiny risk that the radiation used in the screening could cause a cancer.

6

a   From the article, identify the arguments for and against breast cancer screening.

  _____

  _____

  _____

  _____ [2]

b   Use the data in the table, and information in the box at the start of this question, to answer the question below.

Suggest why the government of Swaziland might decide to spend more money diagnosing HIV/AIDs than on breast cancer screening.

	Life expectancy (years)	Estimated population with HIV/ AIDS (%)
Swaziland	32	26
UK	79	0.14

  _____

  _____

  _____ [2]

  Total [4]

Glossary

abundant Abundance measures how common an element is. Silicon is abundant in the lithosphere. Nitrogen is abundant in the atmosphere.

acceleration The rate of change of an object's velocity, that is, its change of velocity per second. In situations where the direction of motion is not important, the change of speed per second tells you the acceleration.

acid A compound that dissolves in water to give a solution with a pH lower than 7. Acid solutions change the colour of indicators, form salts when they neutralize alkalis, react with carbonates to form carbon dioxide, and give off hydrogen when they react with a metal. An acid is a compound that contains hydrogen in its formula and produces hydrogen ions when it dissolves in water.

action at a distance An interaction between two objects that are not in contact, where each exerts a force on the other. Examples include two magnets, two electric charges, or two masses, for example, the Earth and the Moon.

active site The part of an enzyme that the reacting molecules fit into.

active transport Molecules are moved in or out of a cell using energy. This process is used when transport needs to be faster than diffusion, and when molecules are being moved from a region where they are at low concentration to where they are at high concentration.

activity The rate at which nuclei in a sample of radioactive material decay and give out alpha, beta, or gamma radiation.

actual yield The mass of the required chemical obtained after separating and purifying the product of a chemical reaction.

aerobic respiration Respiration that uses oxygen.

air resistance The force exerted on an object by the air, when it moves through it. Its direction is opposite to the direction in which the object is moving.

alkali A compound that dissolves in water to give a solution with a pH higher than 7. An alkali can be neutralised by an acid to form a salt. Solutions of alkalis contain hydroxide ions.

alkali metal An element in Group 1 of the periodic table. Alkali metals react with water to form alkaline solutions of the metal hydroxide.

alpha radiation The least penetrating type of ionising radiation, produced by the nucleus of an atom in radioactive decay. A high-speed helium nucleus.

alternating current (a.c.) An electric current that reverses direction many times a second.

Alzheimer's disease A form of senile dementia caused by irreversible degeneration of the brain.

amino acids The small molecules that are joined in long chains to make proteins. All the proteins in living things are made from 20 different amino acids joined in different orders.

ammeter A meter that measures the size of an electric current in a circuit.

ampere (amp) The unit of electric current.

anaerobic respiration Respiration that does not use oxygen.

atmosphere The layer of gases that surrounds the Earth.

attract Pull towards.

attractive forces (between molecules) Forces that try to pull molecules together. Attractions between molecules are weak. Molecular chemicals have low melting points and boiling points because the molecules are easy to separate.

auxin A plant hormone that affects plant growth and development. For example, auxin stimulates growth of roots in cuttings.

average speed The distance moved by an object divided by the time taken for this to happen.

axon A long, thin extension of the cytoplasm of a neuron. The axon carries electrical impulses very quickly.

background radiation The low-level radiation, mostly from natural sources, that everyone is exposed to all the time, everywhere.

bacterium (plural bacteria) One type of single-celled microorganism. They do not have a nucleus. Some bacteria may cause disease.

balanced equation An equation showing the formulae of the reactants and products. The equation is balanced when there is the same number of each kind of atom on both sides of the equation.

base pairing The bases in a DNA molecule (A, C, G, T) always bond in the same way. A and T always bond together. C and G always bond together.

behaviour Everything an organism does; its response to all the stimuli around it.

beta blockers Drugs that block the receptor sites for the hormone adrenaline. They inhibit the normal effects of adrenaline on the body.

beta radiation One of several types of ionising radiation, produced by the nucleus of an atom in radioactive decay. More penetrating than alpha radiation but less penetrating than gamma radiation. A highspeed electron.

bleach A chemical that can destroy unwanted colours. Bleaches also kill bacteria. A common bleach is a solution of chlorine in sodium hydroxide.

bulk chemicals Chemicals made by industry on a scale of thousands or millions of tonnes per year. Examples are sulfuric acid, nitric acid, sodium hydroxide, ethanol, and ethanoic acid.

burette A graduated tube with taps or valves used to measure the volume of liquids or solutions during quantitative investigations such as titrations.

carbonate A compound that contains carbonate ions, CO_3^{2-}. An example is calcium carbonate, $CaCO_3$.

catalyst A chemical that starts or speeds up a chemical reaction but is not used up in the process.

cell The basic structural and functional unit of all living things.

cell membrane Thin layer surrounding the cytoplasm of a cell. It restricts the passage of substances into and out of the cell.

cell wall Rigid outer layer of plant cells and bacteria.

cellulose The chemical that makes up most of the fibre in food. The human body cannot digest cellulose.

central nervous system In mammals the brain and spinal cord.

cerebral cortex The highly folded outer region of the brain, concerned with conscious behaviour.

chain reaction A process in which the products of one nuclear reaction cause further nuclear reactions to happen, so that more and more reactions occur and more and more product is formed. Depending on how this process is controlled, it can be used in nuclear weapons or the nuclear reactors in power stations.

charged Carrying an electric charge. Some objects (such as electrons and protons) are permanently charged. A plastic object can be charged by rubbing it. This transfers electrons to or from it.

chemical change/reaction A change that forms a new chemical.

chemical equation A summary of a chemical reaction showing the reactants and products with their physical states (see balanced chemical equation).

chemical industry The industry that converts raw materials such as crude oil, natural gas, and minerals into useful products such as pharmaceuticals, fertilisers, paints, and dyes.

Chemical plant An industrial facility used to manufacture chemicals.

chemical properties A chemical property describes how an element or compound interacts with other chemicals, for example, the reactivity of a metal with water.

chemical species The different chemical forms that an element can take, for example, chlorine has three chemical species: atom, molecule, and ion. Each of these forms has distinct properties.

chlorophyll A green pigment found in chloroplasts. Chlorophyll absorbs energy from sunlight for photosynthesis.

chloroplast An organelle found in some plant cells where photosynthesis takes place.

chromosome Long, thin, threadlike structures in the nucleus of a cell made from a molecule of DNA. Chromosomes carry the genes.

clone A new cell or individual made by asexual reproduction. A clone has the same genes as its parent.

collision theory The theory that reactions happen when molecules collide. The theory helps to explain the factors that affect the rates of chemical change. Not all collisions between molecules lead to a reaction.

commutator A device for changing the direction of the electric current through the coil of a motor every half turn. It consists of a ring divided into two halves (a split ring) with two contacts (brushes) touching the two halves.

concentrated solution The concentration of a solution depends on how much dissolved chemical (solute) there is compared with the solvent. A concentrated solution contains a high level of solute to solvent.

concentration The quantity of a chemical dissolved in a stated volume of solution. Concentrations can be measured in grams per litre.

conditioned reflex A reflex where the response is associated with a secondary stimulus, for example, a dog salivates when it hears a bell because it has associated the bell with food.

conditioning Reinforcement of behaviour associated with conditioned reflexes.

conscious To have awareness of surroundings and sensations.

consciousness The awareness of surroundings and sensations.

conservation of energy The fundamental idea that the total amount of energy in the universe is constant, and never increases or decreases. So if something loses energy, one or more other things must have gained the same amount of energy.

contamination (radioactive) Having a radioactive material inside the body, or having it on the skin or clothes.

control rod In a nuclear reactor, rods made of a special material that absorbs neutrons are raised and lowered to control the rate of fission reactions.

coolant In a nuclear reactor, the liquid or gas that circulates through the core and transfers heat to the boiler.

corrosive A corrosive chemical may destroy living tissue on contact.

counter-force A force in the opposite direction to something's motion.

covalent bonding Strong attractive forces that hold atoms together in molecules. Covalent bonds form between atoms of non-metallic elements.

crust (of the Earth) The outer layer of the lithosphere.

crystalline A material with molecules, atoms, or ions lined up in a regular way as in a crystal.

cutting A shoot or leaf taken from a plant, to be grown into a new plant.

cytoplasm Gel enclosed by the cell membrane that contains the cell organelles such as mitochondria.

denatured A change in the usual nature of something. When enzymes are denatured by heat, their structure, including the shape of the active site, is altered.

development How an organism changes as it grows and matures. As a zygote develops, it forms more and more cells. These are organised into different tissues and organs.

diamond A gemstone. A form of carbon. It has a giant covalent structure and is very hard.

diatomic A molecule with two atoms, for example, N_2, O_2, and Cl_2

diffusion Movement of molecules from a region of high concentration to a region of lower concentration.

dilute The concentration of a solution depends on how much dissolved chemical (solute) there is compared with the solvent. A dilute solution contains a low level of solute to solvent.

direct current (d.c.) An electric current that stays in the same direction.

displacement The length and direction of the straight line from the initial position of an object to its position at a later time.

displacement reaction A more reactive halogen will displace a less reactive halogen, for example, chlorine will displace bromide ions to form bromine and chloride ions.

displacement–time graph A useful way of summarising the motion of an object by showing its displacement at every instant during its journey.

Glossary

dissolve Some chemicals dissolve in liquids (solvents). Salt and sugar, for example, dissolve in water.

distance The length of the path along which an object moves.

distance–time graph A useful way of summarising the motion of an object by showing how far it has moved from its starting point at every instant during its journey.

double helix The shape of the DNA molecule, with two strands twisted together in a spiral.

driving force The force pushing something forward, for example, a bicycle.

Ecstasy A recreational drug that increases the concentration of serotonin at the synapses in the brain, giving pleasurable feelings. Long-term effects may include destruction of the synapses.

effector The part of a control system that brings about a change to the system.

electric charge A fundamental property of matter. Electrons and protons are charged particles. Objects become charged when electrons are transferred to or from them, for example, by rubbing.

electric circuit A closed loop of conductors connected between the positive and negative terminals of a battery or power supply.

electric current A flow of charges around an electric circuit.

electric field A region where an electric charge experiences a force. There is an electric field around any electric charge.

electrode A conductor made of a metal or graphite through which a current enters or leaves a chemical during electrolysis. Electrons flow into the negative electrode (cathode) and out of the positive electrode (anode).

electrolysis Splitting up a chemical into its elements by passing an electric current through it.

electrolyte A chemical that can be split up by an electric current when molten or in solution is the electrolyte. Ionic compounds are electrolytes.

electromagnetic induction The name of the process in which a potential difference (and hence often an electric current) is generated in a wire, when it is in a changing magnetic field.

electron A tiny, negatively charged particle, which is part of an atom. Electrons are found outside the nucleus. Electrons have negligible mass and one unit of charge.

electron arrangement The number and arrangement of electrons in an atom of an element.

electrostatic attraction The force of attraction between objects with opposite electric charges.

embryonic stem cell Unspecialised cell in the very early embryo that can divide to form any type of cell, or even a whole new individual. In human embryos the cells are identical and unspecialised up to the eight-cell stage.

end point The point during a titration at which the reaction is just complete. For example, in an acid–alkali titration, the end point is reached when the indicator changes colour. This happens when exactly the right amount of acid has been added to react with all the alkali present at the start.

endothermic An endothermic process takes in energy from its surroundings.

energy level The electrons in an atom have different energies and are arranged at distinct energy levels.

energy-level diagram A diagram to show the difference in energy between the reactants and the products of a reaction.

enzyme A protein that catalyses (speeds up) chemical reactions in living things.

ethanol Waste product from anaerobic respiration in plants and yeast.

exothermic An exothermic process gives out energy to its surroundings.

extraction (of metals) The process of obtaining a metal from a mineral by chemical reduction or electrolysis. It is often necessary to concentrate the ore before extracting the metal.

fatty sheath Fat wrapped around the outside of an axon to insulate neurons from each other.

fermentation Chemical reactions in living organisms that release energy from organic chemicals, such as yeast producing alcohol from the sugar in grapes.

fermenter A large vessel in which microorganisms are grown to make a useful product.

fetus A developing human embryo is referred to as a fetus once it reaches eight weeks after fertilization. A fetus already has all the main organs that it will have at birth.

fine chemicals Chemicals made by industry in smaller quantities than bulk chemicals. Fine chemicals are used in products such as food additives, medicines, and pesticides.

flame colour A colour produced when a chemical is held in a flame. Some elements and their compounds give characteristic colours. Sodium and sodium compounds, for example, give bright yellow flames.

force A push or a pull experienced by an object when it interacts with another. A force is needed to change the motion of an object.

formulae (chemical) A way of describing a chemical that uses symbols for atoms. A formula gives information about the numbers of different types of atom in the chemical. The formula of sulfuric acid, for example, is H_2SO_4.

friction The force exerted on an object due to the interaction between it and another object that it is sliding over. It is caused by the roughness of both surfaces at a microscopic level.

fuel rod A container for nuclear fuel, which enables fuel to be inserted into, and removed from, a nuclear reactor while it is operating.

gametes The sex cells that fuse to form a zygote. In humans, the male gamete is the sperm and the female gamete is the egg.

gamma radiation (gamma rays) The most penetrating type of ionising radiation, produced by the nucleus of an atom in radioactive decay. The most energetic part of the electromagnetic spectrum.

gene A section of DNA giving the instructions for a cell about how to make one kind of protein.

Glossary

gene switching Genes in the nucleus of a cell switch off and are inactive when a cell becomes specialised. Only genes that the cell needs to carry out its particular job stay active.

generator A device that uses motion to generate electricity. It consists of a coil that rotates in a magnetic field. This produces a potential difference across the ends of the coil, which can then be used to provide an electric current.

genetic Factors that are affected by an organism's genes.

genetic variation Differences between individuals caused by differences in their genes. Gametes show genetic variation – they all have different genes.

giant covalent structure A giant, three-dimensional arrangement of atoms that are held together by covalent bonds. Silicon dioxide and diamond have giant covalent structures.

giant ionic lattice The structure of solid ionic compounds. There are no individual molecules, but millions of oppositely charged ions packed closely together in a regular, three-dimensional arrangement.

glands Parts of the body that make enzymes, hormones, and other secretions in the body, for example sweat glands.

glucose Sugar produced during photosynthesis.

graphite A form of carbon. It has a giant covalent structure. It is unusual for a non-metal in that it conducts electricity.

gravitational potential energy The energy stored when an object is raised to a higher point in the Earth's gravitational field.

group Each column in the periodic table is a group of similar elements.

habitat The place where an organism lives.

half-life The time taken for the amount of a radioactive element in a sample to fall to half its original value.

halogens The family name of the Group 7 elements.

harmful A harmful chemical is one that may cause damage to health if swallowed, breathed in, or absorbed through the skin.

high-level waste A category of nuclear waste that is highly radioactive and hot. Produced in nuclear reactors and nuclear-weapons processing.

hormone A chemical messenger secreted by specialised cells in animals and plants. Hormones bring about changes in cells or tissues in different parts of the animal or plant.

hydrogen ion A hydrogen atom that has lost one electron. The symbol for a hydrogen ion is H^+. Acids produce aqueous hydrogen ions, $H^+(aq)$, when dissolved in water.

hydrosphere All the water on Earth. This includes oceans, lakes, rivers, underground reservoirs, and rainwater.

hydroxide ion A negative ion, OH^-. Alkalis give aqueous hydroxide ions when they dissolve in water.

in parallel A way of connecting electric components that makes a branch (or branches) in the circuit so that charges can flow around more than one loop.

in series A way of connecting electric components so that they are all in a single loop. The charges pass through them all in turn.

indicator A chemical that shows whether a solution is acidic or alkaline. For example, litmus turns blue in alkalis and red in acids. Universal indicator has a range of colours that show the pH of a solution.

insoluble Does not form a solution (dissolve) in water or other solutes.

instantaneous speed The speed of an object at a particular instant. In practice, its average speed over a very short time interval.

interaction What happens when two objects collide, or influence each other at a distance. When two objects interact, each experiences a force.

interaction pair Two forces that arise from the same interaction. They are equal in size and opposite in direction, and each acts on a different object.

intermediate-level waste A category of nuclear waste that is generally short-lived but requires some shielding to protect living organisms, for example, contaminated materials that result from decommissioning a nuclear reactor.

involuntary An automatic response made by the body without conscious thought.

ion An electrically charged atom or group of atoms.

ionic bonding Very strong attractive forces that hold the ions together in an ionic compound. The forces come from the attraction between positively and negatively charged ions.

ionic compounds Compounds formed by the combination of a metal and a non-metal. They contain positively charged metal ions and negatively charged non-metal ions.

ionic equation An ionic equation describes a chemical change by showing only the reacting ions in solution.

ionising Able to remove electrons from atoms, producing ions.

ionising radiation Radiation with photons of sufficient energy to remove electrons from atoms in its path. Ionising radiation, such as high energy ultraviolet, X-rays, and gamma rays, can damage living cells.

irradiation Being exposed to radiation from an external source.

isotope Atoms of the same element that have different mass numbers because they have different numbers of neutrons in the nucleus.

kinetic energy The energy that something has owing to its motion.

lactic acid Waste product from anaerobic respiration in animals.

learn To gain new knowledge or skills.

life cycle The stages an organism goes through as it matures, develops, and reproduces.

light intensity The amount of light reaching a given area.

light meter Device for measuring light intensity.

light dependent resistor (LDR) An electric circuit component whose resistance varies depending on the brightness of light falling on it.

limiting factor The factor that prevents the rate of photosynthesis from increasing at a particular time.

This may be light intensity, temperature, carbon dioxide concentration, or water availability.

line spectrum A spectrum made up of a series of lines. Each element has its own characteristic line spectrum.

lithosphere The rigid outer layer of the Earth, made up of the crust and the part of mantle just below it.

lock-and-key model In chemical reactions catalysed by enzymes, molecules taking part in the reaction fit exactly into the enzyme's active site. The active site will not fit other molecules – it is specific. This is like a key fitting into a lock.

long-term memory The part of the memory that stores information for a long period, or permanently.

low-level waste A category of nuclear waste that contains small amounts of short-lived radioactivity, for example, paper, rags, tools, clothing, and filters from hospitals and industry.

magnetic field The region around a magnet, or a wire carrying an electric current, in which magnetic effects can be detected. For example, another small magnet in this region will experience a force and may tend to move.

mantle The layer of rock between the crust and the outer core of the Earth. It is approximately 2900 km thick.

meiosis Cell division that halves the number of chromosomes to produce gametes. The four new cells are genetically different from each other and from the parent cell.

memory The storage and retrieval of information by the brain.

meristem cells Unspecialised cells in plants that can develop into any kind of specialised cell.

metal Elements on the left side of the periodic table. Metals have characteristic properties: they are shiny when polished and they conduct electricity. Some metals react with acids to give salts and hydrogen. Metals are present as positive ions in salts.

metal hydroxide A compound consisting of metal positive ions and hydroxide ions. Examples are sodium hydroxide, NaOH, and magnesium hydroxide, $Mg(OH)_2$.

metal oxide A compound of a metal with oxygen.

metallic bonding Very strong attractive forces that hold metal atoms together in a solid metal.

H The metal atoms lose their outer electrons and form positive ions. The electrons drift freely around the lattice of positive metal ions and hold the ions together.

mineral A naturally occurring element or compound in the Earth's lithosphere.

mitochondrion (plural mitochondria) An organelle in animal and plant cells where respiration takes place.

mitosis Cell division that makes two new cells identical to each other and to the parent cell.

models of memory Explanations for how memory is structured in the brain.

molecular models Models to show the arrangement of atoms in molecules, and the bonds between the atoms.

molecule A group of atoms joined together. Most non-metals consist of molecules. Most compounds of non-metals with other non-metals are also molecular.

molten A chemical in the liquid state. A chemical is molten when the temperature is above its melting point but below its boiling point.

momentum (plural momenta) A property of any moving object. Equal to mass multiplied by velocity.

motor A device that uses an electric current to produce continuous motion.

motor neuron A neuron that carries nerve impulses from the brain or spinal cord to an effector.

H **mRNA** Messenger RNA, a chemical involved in making proteins in cells. The mRNA molecule is similar to DNA but single stranded. It carries the genetic code from the DNA molecule out of the nucleus into the cytoplasm.

multistore model One explanation for how the human memory works.

negative A label used to name one type of charge or one terminal of a battery. It is the opposite of positive.

negative ion An ion that has a negative charge (an anion).

nerve cell A cell in the nervous system that transmits electrical signals to allow communication within the body.

nerve impulses Electrical signals carried by neurons (nerve cells).

nervous system Tissues and organs that control the body's responses to stimuli. In a mammal it is made up of the central nervous system and peripheral nervous system.

neuron Nerve cell.

neuroscientist A scientist who studies how the brain and nerves function.

neutralisation reaction A reaction in which an acid reacts with an alkali to form a salt. During neutralisation reactions, the hydrogen ions in the acid solution react with hydroxide ions in the alkaline solution to make water molecules.

neutron An uncharged particle found in the nucleus of atoms. The relative mass of a neutron is 1.

newborn reflexes Reflexes to particular stimuli that usually occur only for a short time in newborn babies.

nitrate ions An ion is an electrically charged atom or group of atoms. The nitrate ion has a negative charge, NO_3^-.

non-ionising radiation Radiation with photons that do not have enough energy to ionise molecules.

nuclear fission The process in which a nucleus of uranium-235 breaks apart, releasing energy, when it absorbs a neutron.

nuclear fuel In a nuclear reactor, each uranium atom in a fuel rod undergoes fission and releases energy when hit by a neutron.

nuclear fusion The process in which two small nuclei combine to form a larger one, releasing energy. An example is hydrogen combining to form helium. This happens in stars, including the Sun.

nucleus (atom) The tiny central part of an atom (made up of protons and neutrons). Most of the mass of an atom is concentrated in its nucleus.

nucleus (cell) Organelle that contains the chromosomes cells of plants, animals, fungi, and some microorganisms.

ohm The unit of electrical resistance. Symbol Ω.

Ohm's law The result that the current, I, through a resistor, R, is proportional to the voltage, V, across the resistor, provided its temperature remains the same. Ohm's law does not apply to all conductors.

optimum temperature The temperature at which enzymes work fastest.

ore A natural mineral that contains enough valuable minerals to make it profitable to mine.

organelles The specialised parts of a cell, such as the nucleus and mitochondria. Chloroplasts are organelles that occur only in plant cells.

organs Parts of a plant or animal made up of different tissues.

osmosis The diffusion of water across a partially permeable membrane.

oxidation A reaction that adds oxygen to a chemical.

oxide A compound of an element with oxygen.

pancreas An organ in the body that produces some hormones and digestive enzymes. The hormone insulin is made here.

partially permeable membrane A membrane that acts as a barrier to some molecules but allows others to diffuse through freely.

pathway A series of connected neurones that allow nerve impulses to travel along a particular route very quickly.

percentage yield A measure of the efficiency of a chemical synthesis.

period In the context of chemistry, a row in the periodic table.

periodic In chemistry, a repeating pattern in the properties of elements. In the periodic table one pattern is that each period starts with metals on the left and ends with non-metals on the right.

peripheral nervous system The network of nerves connecting the central nervous system to the rest of the body.

pH scale A number scale that shows the acidity or alkalinity of a solution in water.

phloem A plant tissue that transports sugar throughout a plant.

photosynthesis The process in green plants that uses energy from sunlight to convert carbon dioxide and water into the sugar glucose.

phototropism The bending of growing plant shoots towards the light.

physical properties Properties of elements and compounds such as melting point, density, and electrical conductivity. These are properties that do not involve one chemical turning into another.

polymer A material made up of very long molecules. The molecules are long chains of smaller molecules.

positive A label used to name one type of charge, or one terminal of a battery. It is the opposite of negative.

positive ion Ions that have a positive charge (cations).

potential difference (p.d.) The difference in potential energy (for each unit of charge flowing) between any two points in an electric circuit.

power In an electric circuit, the rate at which work is done by the battery or power supply on the components in a circuit. Power is equal to current $\times$ voltage.

precipitate An insoluble solid formed on mixing two solutions. Silver bromide forms as a precipitate on mixing solutions of silver nitrate and potassium bromide.

proportional Two variables are proportional if there is a constant ratio between them.

protein Chemicals in living things that are polymers made by joining together amino acids.

proton Tiny particle present in the nuclei of atoms. Protons are positively charged ($+1$).

proton number The number of protons in the nucleus of an atom (also called the atomic number). In an uncharged atom this also gives the number of electrons.

Prozac A brand name for an antidepressant drug. It increases the concentration of serotonin at the synapses in the brain.

pupil reflex The reaction of the muscles in the pupil to light. The pupil contracts in bright light and relaxes in dim light.

quadrat A square grid of a known area that is used to survey plants in a location. Quadrats come in different sizes up to 1 m^2. The size of quadrat that is chosen depends on the size of the plants and also the area that needs to be surveyed.

radiation A flow of information and energy from a source. Light and infrared are examples. Radiation spreads out from its source, and may be absorbed or reflected by objects in its path. It may also go (be transmitted) through them.

radiation dose A measure, in millisieverts, of the possible harm done to your body, which takes into account both the amount and type of radiation you are exposed to.

radioactive Used to describe a material, atom, or element that produces alpha, beta, or gamma radiation.

radioactive decay The spontaneous change in an unstable element, giving out alpha, beta, or gamma radiation. Alpha and beta emission result in a new element.

radiotherapy Using radiation to treat a patient.

random Of no predictable pattern.

rate of photosynthesis Rate at which green plants convert carbon dioxide and water to glucose in the presence of light.

rate of reaction A measure of how quickly a reaction happens. Rates can be measured by following the disappearance of a reactant or the formation of a product.

reactants The chemicals on the left-hand side of an equation. These chemicals react to form the products.

reacting mass The masses of chemicals that react together, and the masses of products that are formed. Reacting masses are calculated from the balanced symbol equation using relative atomic masses and relative formula masses.

reaction (of a surface) The force exerted by a hard surface on an object that presses on it.

Glossary

reactive metal A metal with a strong tendency to react with chemicals such as oxygen, water, and acids. The more reactive a metal, the more strongly it joins with other elements such as oxygen. So reactive metals are hard to extract from their ores.

receptor The part of a control system that detects changes in the system and passes this information to the processing centre.

receptor molecule A protein (often embedded in a cell membrane) that exactly fits with a specific molecule, bringing about a reaction in the cell.

recycling A range of methods for making new materials from materials that have already been used.

reducing agent A chemical that removes oxygen from another chemical. For example, carbon acts as a reducing agent when it removes oxygen from a metal oxide. The carbon is oxidised to carbon monoxide during this process.

reduction A reaction that removes oxygen from a chemical.

reflex arc A neuron pathway that brings about a reflex response. A reflex arc involves a sensory neuron, connecting neurons in the brain or spinal cord, and a motor neuron.

relative atomic mass The mass of an atom of an element compared to the mass of an atom of carbon. The relative atomic mass of carbon is defined as 12.

relative formula mass The combined relative atomic masses of all the atoms in a formula. To find the relative formula mass of a chemical, you just add up the relative atomic masses of the atoms in the formula.

relay neuron A neuron that carries the impulses from the sensory neuron to the motor neuron.

repel Push apart.

repetition Act of repeating.

repetition of information Saying or writing the same thing several times.

resistance The resistance of a component in an electric circuit indicates how easy or difficult it is to move charges through it.

respiration A series of chemical reactions in cells that release energy for the cell to use.

response Action or behaviour that is caused by a stimulus.

resultant force The sum, taking their directions into account, of all the forces acting on an object.

retina Light-sensitive layer at the back of the eye. The retina detects light by converting light into nerve impulses.

retrieval of information Collecting information from a particular source.

risk The probability of an outcome that is seen as undesirable, associated with some behaviour or process.

risk assessment A check on the hazards involved in a scientific procedure. A full assessment includes the steps to be taken to avoid or reduce the risks from the hazards identified.

rock A naturally occurring solid, made up of one or more minerals.

root hair cell Microscopic cell that increases the surface area for absorption of minerals and water by plant roots.

rooting powder A product used in gardening containing plant hormones. Rooting powder encourages a cutting to form roots.

salt An ionic compound formed when an acid neutralizes an alkali or when a metal reacts with a non-metal.

sample Small part of something that is likely to represent the whole.

sensory neuron A neuron that carries nerve impulses from a receptor to the brain or spinal cord.

serotonin A chemical released at one type of synapse in the brain, resulting in feelings of pleasure.

shell A region in space (around the nucleus of an atom) where there can be electrons.

short-term memory The part of the memory that stores information for a short time.

simple reflex An automatic response made by an animal to a stimulus.

slope The slope of a graph is a measure of its steepness.

small molecules Particles of chemicals that consist of small numbers of atoms bonded together. Chemicals made up of one or more nonmetallic elements and that have low boiling and melting points consist of small molecules.

social behaviour Behaviour that takes place between members of the same species, including humans.

specialised A specialised cell is adapted for a particular job.

spectroscopy The use of instruments to produce and analyse spectra. Chemists use spectroscopy to study the composition, structure, and bonding of elements and compounds.

starch A type of carbohydrate found in bread, potatoes, and rice. Plants produce starch to store the energy food they make by photosynthesis. Starch molecules are a long chain of glucose molecules.

starch grains Microscopic granules of starch forming an energy store in plant cells.

stem cell Unspecialised animal cell that can divide and develop into specialised cells.

sterilisation The process of making something free from live bacteria and other microorganisms.

stimulus A change in the environment that causes a response.

stomata Tiny holes in the underside of a leaf that allow carbon dioxide into the leaf and water and oxygen out of the leaf.

strong (nuclear) force A fundamental force of nature that acts inside atomic nuclei.

sub-atomic particles The particles that make up atoms. Protons, neutrons, and electrons are sub-atomic particles.

surface area (of a solid chemical) The area of a solid in contact with other reactants that are liquids or gases.

sustainable Able to continue over long periods of time.

synapse A tiny gap between neurons that transmits nerve impulses from one neuron to another by means of chemicals diffusing across the gap.

tarnish When the surface of a metal becomes dull or discoloured because it has reacted with the oxygen in the air.

theoretical yield The amount of product that would be obtained in a reaction if all the reactants were converted to products exactly as described by the balanced chemical equation.

H therapeutic cloning Growing new tissues and organs from cloning embryonic stem cells. The new tissues and organs are used to treat people who are ill or injured.

thermistor An electric circuit component whose resistance changes markedly with its temperature. It can therefore be used to measure temperature.

tissue Group of specialised cells of the same type working together to do a particular job.

titration An analytical technique used to find the exact volumes of solutions that react with each other.

toxic A chemical that may lead to serious health risks, or even death, if breathed in, swallowed, or taken in through the skin.

transect A straight line that runs through a location. Data on plant and animal distribution is recorded at regular intervals along the line.

transformer An electrical device consisting of two coils of wire wound on an iron core. An alternating current in one coil causes an everchanging magnetic field that induces an alternating current in the other. Used to 'step' voltage up or down to the level required.

transmitter substance Chemical that bridges the gap between two neurons.

trend A description of the way a property increases or decreases along a series of elements or compounds, which is often applied to the elements (or their compounds) in a group or period.

unspecialised Cells that have not yet developed into one particular type of cell.

unstable The nucleus in radioactive isotopes is not stable. It is liable to change, emitting one of several types of radiation. If it emits alpha or beta radiation, a new element is formed.

velocity The speed of an object in a given direction. Unlike speed, which only has a size, velocity also has a direction.

velocity–time graph A useful way of summarising the motion of an object by showing its velocity at every instant during its journey.

voltage The voltage marked on a battery or power supply is a measure of the 'push' it exerts on charges in an electric circuit. The 'voltage' between two points in a circuit means the 'potential difference' between these points.

voltmeter An instrument for measuring the potential difference between two points in an electric circuit.

work Work is done whenever a force makes something move. The amount of work is force multiplied by distance moved in the direction of the force. This is equal to the amount of energy transferred.

working memory The system in the brain responsible for holding and manipulating information needed to carry out tasks.

xylem Plant tissue that transports water through a plant.

yeast Single-celled fungus used in brewing and baking.

zygote The cell made when a sperm cell fertilises an egg cell in sexual reproduction.

Answers

B4 Workout

1 a

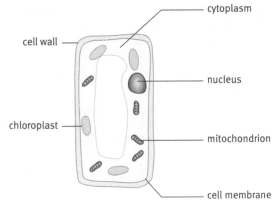

cytoplasm

cell wall

nucleus

chloroplast

mitochondrion

cell membrane

b

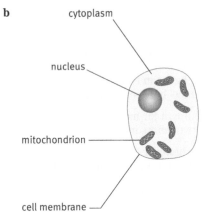

cytoplasm

nucleus

mitochondrion

cell membrane

c

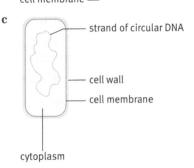

strand of circular DNA

cell wall

cell membrane

cytoplasm

d

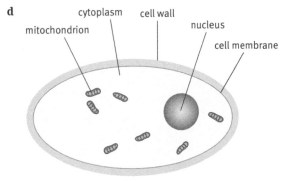

cytoplasm   cell wall

mitochondrion

nucleus

cell membrane

2 B, C, A

3 a Enzyme X
   b pH 1 to pH 4
   c No – the stomach has an acidic environment, but enzyme Y works only in alkaline conditions.

4 a A
   b A
   c A
   d B
   e A and B
   f A and B

B4 Quickfire

1 Movement, respiration, sensitivity, growth, reproduction, excretion, nutrition

2 True statements: **b, e**
   Corrected versions of false statements:
   a The waste process of photosynthesis is oxygen.
   c Aerobic respiration releases more energy per glucose molecule than anaerobic respiration.
   d Enzymes are proteins that speed up chemical reactions.

3 a Carbon dioxide + water $\longrightarrow$ glucose + oxygen
   b Glucose + oxygen $\longrightarrow$ carbon dioxide + water
   c Glucose $\longrightarrow$ lactic acid
   d Glucose $\longrightarrow$ ethanol + carbon dioxide

4 Diffusion: movement of molecules from a region of their higher concentration to one of their lower concentration
   Osmosis: movement of water through a semi-permeable membrane to a region of their higher concentration to one of their lower concentration
   Synthesis: making a chemical with bigger particles from ones with smaller particles

5 Starch, cellulose, glucose, plant, nitrates, proteins

6 In plant roots, when the soil is waterlogged; in bacteria, in deep puncture wounds; in human muscle cells during vigorous exercise

7 a 1.5 units
   b 37 °C
   c 10 °C to 50 °C
   d The shape of the active site changes (the enzyme becomes denatured).

8 a 00:00 (midnight)
   b 12:00 (midday)
   c 12:00 (midday)

9 a $6CO_2 + 6H_2O \longrightarrow C_6H_{12}O_6 + 6O_2$
   b $C_6H_{12}O_6 + 6O_2 \longrightarrow 6CO_2 + 6H_2O$

10 Nitrates, roots, energy, respiration

B4 GCSE-style questions

1 a As time goes on, the height of the dough increases. There is a rapid initial increase that slows to a stop at 16 cm after 20 minutes.
   b i Zita's idea is partly correct – up to the optimum temperature of the enzyme, the higher the temperature, the faster the dough will rise. But above this temperature the enzyme will be denatured, so the dough will not rise at all.
      ii Sam's idea is not correct. The anaerobic respiration reaction of the yeast is not affected by light intensity, though the lamp may increase the temperature.
      iii Tom could add an alkali to the yeast and sugar mixture, and repeat Riana's procedure. He would need to wear eye protection and protective gloves. If his dough rises more than Riana's in the same time, then his idea would be correct.
   c Glucose $\longrightarrow$ ethanol + carbon dioxide
   d Nucleus – the genetic code for making enzymes used in respiration is found here; cytoplasm – the enzymes used in anaerobic respiration are found here; mitochondria – the enzymes found in aerobic respiration are found here.

2 5/6 marks: answer clearly describes how substances move into and out of plant cells by diffusion, including osmosis, **and** explains the processes logically and coherently. All information in the answer is relevant, clear, organised, and presented in a structured and coherent format. Specialist terms are used appropriately. There are few, if any, errors in grammar, punctuation, and spelling.

3/4 marks: answer describes how substances move into and out of plant cells by diffusion, including osmosis, **and** there is some logic and coherence in the answer.

Most of the information is relevant and presented in a structured and coherent format. Specialist terms are usually used correctly. There are occasional errors in grammar, punctuation, and spelling.

1/2 marks: answer briefly describes how substances move into and out of plant cells by diffusion, **but** does not make clear that osmosis is a special case of diffusion **and** the explanation lacks logic and coherence. There may be limited use of specialist terms. Errors of grammar, punctuation, and spelling prevent communication of the science. Answer includes 1 or 2 points of those listed below.

0 marks: insufficient or irrelevant science. Answer not worthy of credit.

Relevant points include:

- Diffusion is the overall movement of molecules from a region of their higher concentration to a region of their lower concentration.
- Diffusion is a passive process – it does not need extra energy.
- Carbon dioxide molecules get into leaves by diffusion.
- Oxygen molecules get out of leaves by diffusion.
- Osmosis is a special case of diffusion.
- Osmosis is the movement of water molecules from a region of their higher concentration to a region of their lower concentration through a partially permeable membrane.
- Water gets into root cells by osmosis.

3 a i Range = 15 to 18 bubbles

  ii

number of bubbles in one minute (y-axis)
distance of plant from lamp (cm) (x-axis)

Points plotted: (20, 49), (40, 35), (60, 21), (80, 17), (100, 13)

  b The closer the lamp is to the plant, the greater the number of bubbles that are produced in one minute. This indicates that the rate of photosynthesis increases as the lamp gets closer.

  c Artem could heat water in kettle, or in a beaker over a Bunsen burner flame, or use a thermostatically controlled water bath. He could measure the rate of bubble production by placing the pondweed in water of different temperatures. He would need a thermometer to measure the temperature of the water. He would need to keep other conditions, such as light intensity, constant.

  d i Carbon dioxide + water $\longrightarrow$ glucose + oxygen
     ii Chloroplast

4 a Martha. To find out how plant species change gradually from one area to another

  b Quadrat A because it includes foxgloves and wild garlic plants, which grow well in shade.

5 a $6CO_2 + 6H_2O \rightarrow C_6H_{12}O_6 + 6O_2$

  b At 0.04% carbon dioxide, as light intensity increases, so does the rate of photosynthesis, up to a certain limit. Above this value, another factor must be limiting the rate of photosynthesis. At the higher concentration of carbon dioxide, the reaction is faster. At this higher concentration, rate increases as light intensity increases, as before. But again the graph becomes horizontal when another factor is in short supply.

  c i Nitrates are used to make amino acids. These are joined together in particular orders to make proteins with different structures and functions.
     ii Plant root hair cells absorb nitrates by active transport across the cell membrane. The process requires energy. First, nitrate ions enter a carrier protein in the membrane. Energy is transferred and the protein changes its shape. This releases the nitrate ion on the other side of the membrane. The carrier protein then goes back to its original shape.

C4 Workout

1 a Column B: corrosive, toxic, oxidising

  b Column C: wear gloves; use in a well-ventilated fume cupboard or wear mask over nose and mouth; keep away from flammable chemicals.

2 Life is fun. So is revision.

3 Picture of a snail.

4 She is beautiful, I think.

5 Red: group 2; blue: period 3; pencil: elements to right of stepped line (elements to the right of a stepped line between aluminium and silicon, germanium and arsenic, and so on); red circle: three from group 1, or hydrogen; blue circle: three from group 7

6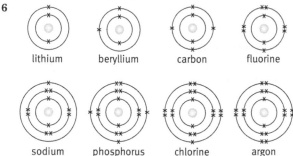

lithium beryllium carbon fluorine

sodium phosphorus chlorine argon

C4 Quickfire

1 Nucleus, neutrons, shells, electrons, electrons, 7, 7

2 a 7
   b 7
   c B
   d 7
   e 1
   f 7

3 a Sodium + water $\longrightarrow$ sodium hydroxide + hydrogen
   b Potassium + chlorine $\longrightarrow$ potassium chloride
   c Hydrogen + iodine $\longrightarrow$ hydrogen iodide
   d Lithium + water $\longrightarrow$ lithium hydroxide + hydrogen
   e Sodium + chlorine $\longrightarrow$ sodium chloride
   f Lithium + bromine $\longrightarrow$ lithium bromide

4 a 11 protons, 12 neutrons, 11 electrons
   b 15 protons, 16 neutrons, 15 electrons
   c 13 protons, 14 neutrons, 13 electrons
   d 23 protons, 28 neutrons, 23 electrons
   e 39 protons, 50 neutrons, 39 electrons

5

Name	Formula
water	H_2O
hydrogen gas	H_2
potassium chloride	KCl
sodium hydroxide	NaOH
iodine	I_2
chlorine gas	Cl_2
potassium bromide	KBr

6 a Reacts:
chlorine + sodium bromide $\longrightarrow$ sodium chloride + bromine
b No reaction
c Reacts:
bromine + sodium iodide $\longrightarrow$ sodium bromide + iodine
d No reaction
e Reacts:
chlorine + potassium iodide $\longrightarrow$ potassium chloride + iodine

7 a 2
b 3
c 6
d 2
e 1 atom of iron and 3 atoms of chlorine

8 a $2K(s) + 2H_2O(l) \longrightarrow 2KOH(aq) + H_2(g)$
b $2Na(s) + Cl_2(g) \longrightarrow 2NaCl(s)$
c $2Li(s) + 2H_2O(l) \longrightarrow 2LiOH(aq) + H_2(g)$
d $2K(s) + Cl_2(g) \longrightarrow 2KCl(s)$
e $2Fe(s) + 3Cl_2(g) \longrightarrow 2FeCl_3(s)$

9 a NaBr
b KCl
c MgS
d K_2O

10 a Sr^{2+}
b Be^{2+}

C4 GCSE-style questions

1 a Strontium is in group 2 of the periodic table, like calcium. So it is likely to react in a similar way to calcium.
b i 2.8.8.2
ii 2
c i Any number between 715 and 849 is acceptable.
ii Data from the column *reaction with water* shows that, as you go down the group, the reactions get more vigorous.
d Strontium + water $\longrightarrow$ strontium hydroxide + hydrogen
e i 1
ii 2
iii 4

2 a The melting points decrease as the group is descended.
b The prediction is incorrect. This decreases confidence in the explanation.
c 5/6 marks: answer clearly identifies the extent to which each set of data supports, or does not support, Ben's explanation **and** includes a reasoned assessment of whether or not the data, overall, do or do not support the explanation.
All information in the answer is relevant, clear, organised, and presented in a structured and coherent format. Specialist terms are used appropriately. There are few, if any, errors in grammar, punctuation, and spelling.

3/4 marks: answer identifies the extent to which one or both sets of data supports, or do not support, Ben's explanation **and** includes a brief assessment of the overall value of the data in supporting the explanation. Most of the information is relevant and presented in a structured and coherent format. Specialist terms are usually used correctly. There are occasional errors in grammar, punctuation, and spelling.
1/2 marks: answer explains how one or other of the data sets supports, or does not support, the explanation **and** the explanation lacks detail/clarity. There may be limited use of specialist terms. Errors of grammar, punctuation, and spelling prevent communication of the science. Answer includes 1 or 2 points of those listed below.
0 marks: insufficient or irrelevant science. Answer not worthy of credit.
Relevant points include:
- Most of the data for the group 1 metal chlorides shows that as ion size increases, melting point decreases.
- The data for lithium does not fit this pattern.
- Overall, for the group 1 metal chlorides, the data supports the explanation.
- The data for the group 2 metal chlorides shows that as ion size increases, the melting point of the chloride increases.
- The group 2 metal chloride data does not support Ben's explanation at all.
- Overall, since one set of data supports the explanation and one set of data does not support the explanation, the data cannot be said to support Ben's explanation.

3 a i

Sodium	11	11	10	Na^+
Fluorine/fluoride	9	9	10	F^-

ii

b The sodium and fluoride ions separate from each other and are free to move independently in the water.
c The sodium and fluoride ions are charged particles that are free to move independently.

4 a i 19
ii 19
b Potassium

5 a NaBr
b $Cl_2(aq) + 2NaBr(aq) \longrightarrow 2NaCl(aq) + Br_2(l)$

P4 Workout

1 a F
b T
c F
d T
e F
f T

2 Rope 10 N to right; tricycle 120 N to right; trolley no resultant force

3 Left picture: C; middle picture: B; right picture: A

4 In order along the curve: B, A, C, E, D, F

5 1 interaction; 2 kinetic; 3 acceleration; 4 resultant; 5 friction; 6 average; 7 reaction; 8 potential; 9 driving; 10 momentum; 11 negative

P4 Quickfire

1 Average, time, short, gravity, upwards, constant
2 a T
   b T
   c T
   d F
   e T
   f T
   g F
3 a Greater
   b Ali, the weight
   c Less, heating
4 a 200 m/min
   b 40 m/s
   c 18 m/s
   d 4 cm/s
5 a 5 m/s^2
   b 2 m/s^2
6 a 88 000 kg m/s
   b 304 kg m/s
   c 13.5 kg m/s
7 15 000 Ns
8 a 30 000 J
   b 1 250 000 J
   c 58 J
9 A jet engine draws in air at the front and pushes it out at the back. An equal and opposite force pushes the engine forward. This is the driving force.
10 In order along the curve: A, B, D, F, E, C

P4 GCSE-style questions

1 a i All statements are true except the first one.
      ii 1500 J
      iii 1500 J
   b 300 J
2 5/6 marks: answer explains in detail why the driving force needed by lorry B is less than the driving force needed by lorry A **and** the explanation is logical and coherent.
   All information in the answer is relevant, clear, organised, and presented in a structured and coherent format. Specialist terms are used appropriately. There are few, if any, errors in grammar, punctuation, and spelling.
   3/4 marks: answer explains why the driving force needed by lorry B is less than the driving force needed by lorry A **but** the answer lacks detail **or** the explanation lacks clarity and coherence.
   Most of the information is relevant and presented in a structured and coherent format. Specialist terms are usually used correctly. There are occasional errors in grammar, punctuation, and spelling.
   1/2 marks: answer gives some reasons to explain the difference in driving force **and** the explanation lacks detail **and** the answer lacks clarity and coherence.
   There may be limited use of specialist terms. Errors of grammar, punctuation, and spelling prevent communication of the science. Answer includes 1 or 2 points of those listed below.
   0 marks: insufficient or irrelevant science. Answer not worthy of credit.
   Relevant points to include:
   • For the lorry to travel in a straight line at a steady speed, the driving force needs to be equal to the counter force.

   • The counter force is made up of friction and air resistance.
   • The frictional force between the road and the lorry is the same for each lorry.
   • Lorry B experiences less air resistance.
   • So the counter force on lorry B is less.
   • So the driving force needed by lorry B is less.
3 a i D to E
      ii Stationary from B to C; moving at a steady speed from C to D – this is the fastest part of the fire engine's journey.
      iii 1 km/min
   b 12 m/s
4 a F = cat and G = horse
   b Animal A top speed = 3 m/s; animal B top speed = 6 m/s
   c Correct statements: the top speed of animal B is twice the top speed of animal A; animal C is unlikely to be a pig.
5 a
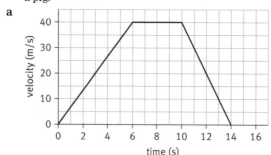
   b 6.7 m/s
   c The velocity changes from 30 m/s in one direction to 30 m/s in the opposite direction.
   d i 100 m
      ii The motorbike is travelling at a steady speed of 13.3 m/s

B5 Workout

1 1 testes, meiosis, 4, sperm
   2 23
   3 ovaries, meiosis, eggs
   4 23
   5 fertilisation
   6 zygote, 23, 46
   7 mitosis, 2, 46
   8 2, 4
   9 4, 8
   10 stem
   11 16
2 Auxin, chromosomes, embryonic, fetus, gametes, mitochondria, nucleus, organelles, phototropism, tissues, unspecialised, xylem, young, zygote
3

	Meiosis	Mitosis
What does it make?	gametes (sex cells)	body cells
How many new cells does each parent cell make?	4	2
How many chromosomes are in each cell?	half as many as in the parent cell	same as in the parent cell
Where does it happen?	in sex organ cells	in body cells
Why does it happen?	to make sex cells for sexual reproduction	so an organism can grow, and replace damaged cells

Answers

B5 Quickfire

1 a P
   b B
   c P
   d B
   e B
   f P

2 Organelles, mitochondria, chromosomes, DNA, strands, mitosis, chromosomes, cell

3

Species	Number of chromosomes in sex cell	Number of chromosomes in body cell
horse	32	64
wolf	39	78
carp	52	104
human (other answers are possible)	23	46

4 A – T, T – A, C – G, G – C

5 True statements: **b, e, f, i, j**
   Corrected versions of false statements:
   a Up to the 8-cell stage, all the cells in a human embryo are identical.
   c Adult stem cells can become many, but not all, types of cell needed by a human.
   d A zygote divides by mitosis to form an embryo.
   g Groups of specialised cells in an animal are called tissues.
   h Cell division by meiosis produces new cells that are not identical to the parent cell.

6

Cell	Are these genes switched on?		
	gene to make keratin	gene to make salivary amylase	gene for respiration
nail	yes	no	yes
hair	yes	no	yes
embryonic stem cell	yes	yes	yes
salivary gland cell	no	yes	yes
muscle cell	no	no	yes

7 a Nucleus
   b Cytoplasm
   c Mitochondria

8 a Light from the right; highest concentration of auxins on left of bent part of shoot
   b Light from the left; highest concentration of auxins on right of bent part of shoot
   c Light from above; concentration of auxins similar in all parts of shoot

9 Messenger RNA

10 The order of bases in a gene is the code for building up amino acids in the correct order to make a particular protein.

B5 GCSE-style questions

1 a Gametes, testes, 4, different, 15
   b i Egg or ovum
      ii Fertilisation
   c C, A, D, B

2 a i They can grow many new plants quickly and cheaply; they can reproduce a plant with exactly the features they want.
      ii Auxins
   b i Top row: 6; bottom row: 2
      ii Taking several readings means that a mean can be calculated. This is a better estimate of the quantity than taking one reading alone.
      iii The cuttings with rooting powder grew more roots than those without. This suggests that rooting powder may contain a substance that helps plant stems to grow roots.
   c The graph shows that, for roots and stems, growth increases as auxin concentration increases up to a maximum concentration. Above this concentration, growth decreases steadily from the maximum. The auxin concentrations at which this happens is greater for stems than for roots.

3 a i Stem cells are unspecialised cells. They divide and develop into specialised cells.
      ii They will grow heart muscle cells from the stem cells.
      iii A coherent argument for or against removing and storing umbilical cord blood.
   b i One of: embryos, adults
      ii One of (embryos) ethical objections, problem of rejection; (adults) difficult to separate from other cells, problem of rejection

4 5/6 marks: answer describes several differences between meiosis **and** mitosis and the descriptions of differences are clear and detailed.
   All information in the answer is relevant, clear, organised, and presented in a structured and coherent format. Specialist terms are used appropriately. There are few, if any, errors in grammar, punctuation, and spelling.
   3/4 marks: answer gives several differences between mitosis and meiosis **but** the answer lacks detail **or** answer gives one or two differences between mitosis and meiosis **and** the descriptions of the differences are clear and detailed.
   Most of the information is relevant and presented in a structured and coherent format. Specialist terms are usually used correctly. There are occasional errors in grammar, punctuation, and spelling.
   1/2 marks: answer gives one or two differences between mitosis and meiosis **and** the descriptions of the differences lack detail.
   There may be limited use of specialist terms. Errors of grammar, punctuation, and spelling prevent communication of the science. Answer includes 1 or 2 points of those listed below.
   Relevant points include:
   • Meiosis happens in sex organs; mitosis happens in all other body cells.
   • Meiosis makes four new cells from one parent cell; mitosis makes two new cells.
   • Meiosis makes gametes (sex cells); mitosis makes body cells.
   • Meiosis makes cells with different genetic information. Mitosis makes genetically identical cells.
   • Meiosis makes cells with half the number of chromosomes as are in the parent cell. Mitosis makes cells with the same number of chromosomes as the parent cell.
   • Meiosis happens so that an organism can reproduce. Mitosis happens so that an organism can grow and replace damaged tissues.

5 5/6 marks: answer explains in detail why many genes are inactive in a specialised body cell **and** the explanation is logical and coherent.

All information in the answer is relevant, clear, organised, and presented in a structured and coherent format. Specialist terms are used appropriately. There are few, if any, errors in grammar, punctuation, and spelling.

3/4 marks: answer explains why many genes are inactive in a specialised body cell **but** the answer lacks detail **or** the explanation lacks logic and coherence.

Most of the information is relevant and presented in a structured and coherent format. Specialist terms are usually used correctly. There are occasional errors in grammar, punctuation, and spelling.

1/2 marks: answer briefly explains why many genes are inactive in a specialised body cell **and** the answer lacks detail **and** the explanation lacks logic and coherence. There may be limited use of specialist terms. Errors of grammar, punctuation, and spelling prevent communication of the science. Answer includes 1 or 2 points of those listed below.

0 marks: insufficient or irrelevant science. Answer not worthy of credit.

Relevant points include:

- In a specialised body cell, many genes are switched off because the cell only makes the proteins it needs for its functions.
- When cloning a mammal, inactive genes can be reactivated (switched on).
- This may happen when the nucleus of an egg cell is removed.
- The nucleus is replaced with one from the individual to be cloned.
- The egg cell divides by mitosis to makes an embryo.
- Stem cells from the embryo can be put in a dish of nutrients.
- These stem cells can develop into the type of tissue required.

C5 Workout

1 Box 1: A, oxygen (O_2(g)), argon (Ar(g)), carbon dioxide (CO_2(g)), nitrogen (N_2)(g)
Box 2: B, sodium chloride, potassium bromide, magnesium chloride, water
Box 3: C, silicon dioxide, aluminium oxide

2 Ab1; Ad1; Aii10; Ba2; Bh9; Bii10; Cc3; Ce6; Cf8; Ch4; Da5; Dg7

C5 Quickfire

1 a Oxygen
b Nitrogen
c Oxygen
d Oxygen
e Aluminium

2 CO_2: molecule D
H_2O: molecule A
O_2: molecule B
Ar: atom C

3 Carbon, covalent, four, covalent, hard, three, covalent, slippery, lubricant, can

4 a Zinc oxide + carbon $\longrightarrow$ zinc + carbon dioxide
b Copper oxide + carbon $\longrightarrow$ copper + carbon dioxide

5 a Iron oxide is reduced (red), carbon is oxidised (blue).
b Tin oxide is reduced (red), carbon is oxidised (blue).

6 A, C, B, D, E

7 Nitrogen: simple covalent: –196
Silicon dioxide: giant covalent: 2230
Sodium chloride: giant ionic: 1413

8 a $2ZnO(s) + C(s) \longrightarrow 2Zn(l) + CO_2(g)$
b $2Fe_2O_3(s) + 3C(s) \longrightarrow 4Fe(l) + 3CO_2(g)$
c $2CuO(s) + C(s) \longrightarrow 2Cu(l) + CO_2(g)$

9 a $Pb^{2+}(aq) + 2I^-(aq) \longrightarrow PbI_2(s)$
b $Cu^{2+}(aq) + 2OH^-(aq) \longrightarrow Cu(OH)_2(s)$

10 a 130 tonnes
b 27 kg

C5 GCSE-style questions

1 a Zn^{2+}
b Salt B
c Calcium bromide. Test with sodium hydroxide solution shows that salt A contains Ca^{2+} ions. Test with sodium hydroxide solution shows that the salt includes Br– ions.
d If hydrochloric acid were added, chloride ions would be present in the solution, so the solution would test positive for chloride ions, whether or not they were present in the original salt.
e $Ag^+(aq) + Cl^-(aq) \longrightarrow AgCl(s)$

2 5/6 marks: answer clearly explains why the properties of diamond make it suitable for drill tips **and** the explanation is logical and coherent.

All information in the answer is relevant, clear, organised, and presented in a structured and coherent format. Specialist terms are used appropriately. There are few, if any, errors in grammar, punctuation, and spelling.

3/4 marks: answer explains why the properties of diamond make it suitable for drill tips **but** the answer lacks detail **or** the explanation lacks logic and coherence.

Most of the information is relevant and presented in a structured and coherent format. Specialist terms are usually used correctly. There are occasional errors in grammar, punctuation, and spelling.

1/2 marks: answer briefly explains why the properties of diamond make it suitable for drill tips **and** the answer lacks detail **and** the explanation lacks logic and coherence. There may be limited use of specialist terms. Errors of grammar, punctuation, and spelling prevent communication of the science. Answer includes 1 or 2 points of those listed below.

0 marks: insufficient or irrelevant science. Answer not worthy of credit.

Relevant points include:

- Diamond is very hard.
- So its surface cannot be worn down by other materials, which makes it a suitable material for drill tips.
- Diamond has a giant covalent structure.
- The covalent bonds between each carbon atom and its four neighbours are very strong.
- The strength of the covalent bonds means that they are difficult (require large amounts of energy) to break.
- Scratching diamond would involve breaking some covalent bonds at its surface.
- The large amounts of energy needed to break these bonds mean that diamond is very hard.

3 a i It has a lower boiling point than the other materials on the bar chart, showing that the forces that must be overcome in order to make the liquid boil are relatively weak.
ii Iodine
b i X or Z because they do not conduct electricity when solid.
ii Does the substance conduct electricity when liquid or in solution? If either X or Z does, then it is an ionic compound.

   c **i**   W

      ii It conducts electricity when solid.

4 **a** **i**   Hydrosphere

      ii When solid, it does not conduct electricity – the charged particles cannot move; it has a high melting point – there are strong attractive forces between the ions; when solid it forms crystals – the ions are arranged in a regular pattern; when liquid, it conducts electricity – the charged particles can move independently.

     iii $MgBr_2$

   b 76.9 m^3

   c **i**   An electric current decomposes the electrolyte. An electric current passes through liquid magnesium chloride.

      ii Magnesium is too reactive to be reduced by carbon – the ionic bonds in magnesium oxide are very strong.

5 **a** 176

   b 14 g

6 **a** Giant, strong.

   b **i**   C

      ii E

7 **a** **i**

'sea' of freely moving electrons   lattice of positive ions

      ii Aluminium is a good conductor of electricity because it has charged particles (electrons) that are free to move.
It is malleable because its layers of ions can slide over each other.

   b **i**   529 t

      ii 5/6 marks: all information in the answer is relevant, clear, organised, and presented in a structured and coherent format. Specialist terms are used appropriately. Few, if any, errors in grammar, punctuation, and spelling. Answer includes 5 or 6 points from those below.
3/4 marks: most of the information is relevant and presented in a structured and coherent format. Specialist terms are usually used correctly. There are occasional errors in grammar, punctuation, and spelling. Answer includes 3 or 4 points from those below.
1/2 marks: answer may be simplistic. There may be limited use of specialist terms. Errors of grammar, punctuation, and spelling prevent communication of the science. Answer includes 1 or 2 points from those below.
Points to include:
- Molten aluminium oxide is poured into an electrolysis cell.
- The cell has graphite electrodes.
- When a current flows through the liquid, positive aluminium ions move towards the negative electrode.

- Here they gain electrons to form neutral atoms.
- These atoms make up aluminium liquid, which is collected through a tap in the electrolysis cell.
- Negative oxide ions move towards the positive electrode.
- Here they lose electrons to become neutral atoms.
- Oxygen atoms join together in pairs to become oxygen molecules.

P5 Workout

1 Clockwise from top: volts, the same as, voltage, push, less

2 **a** $A_1 = A_2 = 100$ mA

   b **i**   Resistor on right

      ii Greatest; ... more work is done by charge flowing through a large resistance than through a small one

   c **i**   0.6 V

      ii ...the p.d.s across the components add up to the p.d. across the battery

3 **a** B

   b A

   c B

4 1 resistance, 2 current, 3 ohm, 4 power, 5 V, 6 parallel, 7 voltmeter, 8 Ω, 9 generator, 10 induction, 11 R, 12 direct, 14 A, 15 commutator, 16 DC

P5 Quickfire

1 Ammeter (A); voltmeter (V); cell —|⊢ ;

   power supply —|⊢|⊢ (battery) or —+ ⁻— (DC)

   or —o~o— (AC); lamp ⊗; switch —o╱o— ;

   LDR —▱—; fixed resistor —▭—;

   variable resistor —▱—; thermistor —▱—

2 All conductors...contain charges that are free to move; insulators...do not conduct electricity; insulators... do not contain charges that are free to move; metal conductors... contain charges that are free to move; metal conductors... contain electrons that are free to move; in a complete circuit... charges are not used up; in a complete circuit...the battery makes free charges flow in a continuous loop.

3 Hotter, more, smaller

4 **a** X

   b Y

   c Y

   d B

   e B

   f X

5 Coil, current, out, pole

6

7 **a** 920 W

   b 207 W

8 11.5 V

9 **a** Resistors get hotter when a current flows through them because there are collisions between the moving charges and the stationary ions in the wire.

b The potential difference is largest across the component with the greatest resistance because more work is done by the charge moving through a large resistance than through a small one.

c Mains electricity is supplied as a.c. because it is easier to generate than d.c. and simpler to distribute over long distances.

P5 GCSE-style questions

1 a i Voltmeter connected in parallel across the heater.
  ii 1.2 Ω
b The wire gets hotter because moving electrons bump into stationary ions in the wire.
2 5/6 marks: answer clearly explains why the coil rotates continuously **and** the explanation is logical and coherent. All information in the answer is relevant, clear, organised, and presented in a structured and coherent format. Specialist terms are used appropriately. There are few, if any, errors in grammar, punctuation, and spelling.
3/4 marks: answer explains why the coil rotates continuously **but** the answer lacks detail **or** the explanation lacks logic and coherence.
Most of the information is relevant and presented in a structured and coherent format. Specialist terms are usually used correctly. There are occasional errors in grammar, punctuation, and spelling.
1/2 marks: answer briefly explains why the coil rotates continuously and the answer lacks detail and the explanation lacks logic and coherence.
There may be limited use of specialist terms. Errors of grammar, punctuation, and spelling prevent communication of the science. Answer includes 1 or 2 points of those listed below.
0 marks: insufficient or irrelevant science. Answer not worthy of credit.
Relevant points include:
- There are forces on the sides of the coil, because the currents in these are at right angles to the magnetic field lines.
- One of these forces is up, and the other is down, because the currents in the two sides of the coil are in opposite directions.
- These forces make the coil turn.
- The commutator swaps the current direction every time the coil is vertical.
- This reverses the forces, and makes the coil rotate continuously.

3 a Three from: increase the number of coils, increase the strength of the magnet, put an iron core inside the coil, unwind/spin the magnet more rapidly
b i The two coils of wire are wound around an iron core. A changing current in one coil causes a changing magnetic field in the iron core, which in turn induces a changing potential difference across the other transformer coil. The coil on the left has more turns, so the current in this coil is greater.
  ii 120
4 a i 230 V
  ii 230 V
b 3.3 amps
c Stays the same
d i 14.4 V
  ii Fridge: current is smallest through this appliance, whilst the voltage across all the appliances is the same.

5 a Resistor J 3 Ω; K 30 Ω; L 60 Ω; M 2 Ω
b i Resistance $= \dfrac{1}{(0.2 \div 12)} = 60\,\Omega$
  ii Resistor L
c The resistance calculated from the graph is 2 Ω. This increases confidence that the resistance calculated in part (a) is correct, since the value is the same.
6 a 0.025 A
b The potential difference across the three components add up to the potential difference across the battery because the work done on each unit of charge by the battery must equal the work done by it on the circuit components.
c The buzzer, because the potential difference is largest across the component with the greatest resistance.
d The potential difference across the buzzer decreases.
e i The resistor
  ii In Mary's circuit, the p.d. across the resistor was smaller than the p.d.s over the other components, showing that the resistor had the smallest resistance. In the parallel circuit the p.d. across all the components is the same. The largest current flows through the component with the smallest resistance.

B6 Workout

1 Behaviour – anything an animal does; stimulus – a change in the environment; response – an action caused by a change in the environment
2 Left from top: motor neuron, sensory neuron, effector, receptor
Right from top: spinal cord
3 Nucleus: controls cell; cytoplasm: cell reactions happen here; cell membrane: substances get into and out of the cell through this; fatty sheath: insulates neuron from neighbouring cells; branched endings: make connections with other neurons or effectors
4 Correct order: middle, top, bottom.
Notes for middle diagram: a nerve impulse gets to the end of the sensory neuron; notes for top diagram: the sensory neuron releases a chemical into the synapse and the chemical diffuses across the synapse; notes for bottom diagram: the chemical arrives at receptor molecules on the motor neuron's membrane and the chemical's molecules bind to the receptor molecules. This stimulates a nerve impulse in the motor neuron.
5 Bird: those caterpillars are poisonous. She won't eat them again because they taste so bad. Caterpillar: she's learnt that caterpillars like us don't taste good – so that's one less bird that's going to try to eat me.

B6 Quickfire

1 a S
 b C
 c S
 d C
2 a Brain and spinal cord
 b Motor neuron and sensory neuron
3 Electrical impulse – travels quickly and brings about short-term changes; hormone – travels in the blood and brings about long-term changes
4 A, F, C, D, E, B
5 a S
 b S
 c E
 d E
 e S
 f S
 g E

6   a   Brains
    b   Neurons
    c   Consciousness, language, intelligence, memory
    d   Studying patients with brain damage, electrically stimulating parts of the brain, doing MRI scans

7   A, E, C, D, B, F, G

8   True statements: **b, d, f**
    Corrected versions of false statements:
    a   Long-term memory is a seemingly limitless store of information *or* short-term memory has a limit to the information it can store.
    c   Repetition moves information from your short-term memory to your long-term memory.
    e   Your sensory memory stores memories linked to sounds and visual information.

9   a   Reflex responses are automatic and very quick since no processing of information is required.
    b   Ecstasy blocks the sites in the brain's synapses where serotonin, a transmitter substance, is removed.
    c   Conditioned reflexes increase an animal's chance of survival because they enable the animal to learn new things.
    d   Mammals can adapt to new situations because there is a huge variety of potential pathways in the brain.

B6 GCSE-style questions

1   a   She grips a finger that is put into the palm of her hand, she steps when her feet touch a flat surface
    b   ...something being put into her mouth; milk
    c   Reflex actions help a worm to respond to stimuli in ways that are most likely to result in their survival, for example in finding food and sheltering from predators.

2   5/6 marks: answer describes several methods that help humans to remember information **and** includes a detailed, logical, and coherent explanation for each method.
    All information in the answer is relevant, clear, organised, and presented in a structured and coherent format. Specialist terms are used appropriately. Few, if any, errors in grammar, punctuation, and spelling.
    3/4 marks: answer describes one or two methods that help humans to remember information **and** includes an explanation for each method **but** the explanations lacks detail, logic, and coherence **or** includes an explanation for one method **and** the explanation is detailed, coherent, and logical.
    Most of the information is relevant and presented in a structured and coherent format. Specialist terms are usually used correctly. There are occasional errors in grammar, punctuation, and spelling.
    1/2 marks: answer describes one method that helps humans to remember information **and** gives an explanation for this method **or** the answer describes one method which helps humans to remember information **but** does not include an explanation for this method.
    There may be limited use of specialist terms. Errors of grammar, punctuation, and spelling prevent communication of the science. Answer includes 1 or 2 points of those listed below.
    0 marks: insufficient or irrelevant science. Answer not worthy of credit.
    Relevant points include:
    •   Looking for patterns in the information
    •   This is an example of processing information deeply, which helps humans to remember things
    •   Repeating the information many times
    •   This moves information from the short-term memory to the long-term memory

•   Attaching a strong stimulus to the information, including colour, light, smell

3   a   i   Top line 48, bottom line 32
        ii   Drinking caffeine appears to speed up reaction times.
        iii Because it takes time for messages to travel around a reflex arc.
    b   i   The investigation shows that, under the conditions of the test, reaction times are slower if loud music is playing.
        ii   Kate might not approve of drinking alcohol or Kate might have to drive home or any other sensible answer.

4   a   Effector cells – make changes in response to stimulus; receptor cells – detect a stimulus; brain and spinal cord – control the body's response to a stimulus
    b   i   1 sensory neuron, 2 central nervous system, 3 motor neuron
        ii   Electrical, peripheral, central

5   The dolphin jumps through a hoop for the first time. A nerve impulse travels along a neuron pathway in the brain for the first time. This makes connections between these neurons. The dolphin jumps through the hoop again. More nerve impulses travel along the same neuron pathway. This makes the connections between the neurons in the pathway stronger. It is now easier for nerve impulses to travel along the pathway, and for the dolphin to jump through hoops.

6   a   A nerve impulse arrives at the synapse. A chemical is released from the sensory neuron. The chemical diffuses across the synapse. Molecules of the chemical fit into receptor molecules on the motor neuron. A nerve impulse is stimulated in the motor neuron. The chemical is absorbed back into the sensory neuron to be used again.
    b   i   Cocaine might act in the same way as Ecstasy, blocking the reuptake of serotonin by sensory neurons in synapses.
        ii   If there is a greater concentration of serotonin in synapses, then the transmission of nerve impulses will increase.

C6 Workout

1   Food additives e.g. saccharin; pharmaceuticals e.g. paracetamol; fertilisers e.g. ammonium nitrate; plastics e.g. polythene

2   a   Petrochemicals and polymers
    b   38%
    c   4%

3   From left to right: B, C, A

4   1 acid or alkali; 2 titration flask; 3 solid sample; 4 burette; 5 pure water

5   1 desiccator, 2 crystallisation, 3 end point, 4 catalyst, 5 hydroxide, 6 slower, 7 sulfuric, 8 nitrate, 9 salt

C6 Quickfire

1

Gas	Liquid	Solid
hydrogen chloride	ethanoic sulfuric nitric	tartaric citric

2   a   Acid
    b   Alkali
    c   Acid
    d   Alkali
    e   Both
    f   Both
    g   Both

3

Change	The reaction gets ...		
	faster	slower	can't tell
a Use bigger lumps of calcium carbonate.		√	
b Use more concentrated acid.	√		
c Heat the reaction mixture.	√		
d Use bigger lumps of calcium carbonate and heat the mixture.			√
e Add a catalyst.	√		

4　**a**　Relative atomic mass is the mass of an atom of an element relative to the masses of other atoms.

　　b　An exothermic reaction is one which gives out energy / transfers energy to the surroundings.

5　96%

6

Name of chemical	Formula	Relative formula mass
nitrogen gas	N_2	28
nitric acid	HNO_3	63
magnesium sulfate	$MgSO_4$	120
potassium chloride	KCl	74.5
calcium chloride	$CaCl_2$	111
sodium carbonate	Na_2CO_3	106
calcium carbonate	$CaCO_3$	100

7

Formula of product	Actual yield	Theoretical yield	Percentage yield
SrO	98 kg	104 kg	94
Al_2O_3	222 g	224 g	99
SF_6	68 t	73 t	93

8　**a**　+2

　　b　+3

9

Name of salt	Formula of acid used to make the salt	Formula of hydroxide used to make the salt	Formula of salt
potassium chloride	HCl	KOH	KCl
sodium sulfate	H_2SO_4	$NaOH$	Na_2SO_4
calcium nitrate	HNO_3	$Ca(OH)_2$	$Ca(NO_3)_2$
lithium chloride	HCl	$LiOH$	$LiCl$

1　**a**　$NaOH + HCl \longrightarrow NaCl + H_2O$
　　　　　40 g　　36.5 g　　58.5 g　18 g

　　b　$2KOH + H_2SO_4 \longrightarrow K_2SO_4 + 2H_2O$
　　　　　112 g　　98 g　　　174 g　　36 g

　　c　$2Mg + O_2 \longrightarrow 2MgO$
　　　　　48 g　32 g　　　80 g

　　d　$4Li + O_2 \longrightarrow 2Li_2O$
　　　　　28 g　32 g　　　60 g

　　e　$AgNO_3 + NaCl \longrightarrow AgCl + NaNO_3$
　　　　　170 g　　58.5 g　　143.5 g　　85 g

　　f　$Pb(NO_3)_2 + 2KCl \longrightarrow PbCl_2 + 2KNO_3$
　　　　　331 g　　　149 g　　　278 g　　202 g

　　g　$Fe_2O_3 + 3C \longrightarrow 3CO + 2Fe$
　　　　　160 g　36 g　　　84 g　112 g

　　h　$CaCO_3 \longrightarrow CaO + CO_2$
　　　　　100 g　　　56 g　　44 g

C6 GCSE-style questions

1　**a**　**i**　$2HCl(aq) + CaCO_3(s) \rightarrow CaCl_2(aq) + CO_2(g) + H_2O(l)$

　　　　ii　100 g of calcium carbonate produces 44 g of carbon dioxide, so 1.60 g of carbon dioxide is produced from 3.64 g of calcium carbonate.

　　b　Rate = 1.10 ÷ 1 = 1.10 g/min

　　c　**i**　Experiment Y or experiment Z because both proceeded more slowly than the original experiment.

　　　　ii　Two from: increased temperature; increased acid concentration; used smaller pieces of calcium carbonate/calcium carbonate powder

　　d　Two from: the reaction is exothermic; the energy stored in the reactants is greater than the energy stored in the products; energy is released/given out in the reaction.

2　**a**　Jude's data are more likely to give a value that is closest to the true value because he has collected a set of repeated values of the volume from which he can calculate a mean.

　　b　**i**　Run 2, 11.90; run 3, 12.00; run 4, 12.10; run 5, 15.00

　　　　ii　Outlier is the value for run 5 (15.00 cm^3).

　　　　iii　He had good reason to suspect that the outlier was inaccurate.

　　c　Mean = (11.9 + 12.00 + 12.10) ÷ 3 = 12.00 cm^3

　　d　The results do not support the claim on the blackcurrant drink carton. The results show that the blackcurrant drink contains less vitamin C than orange juice, not four times as much.

3　**a**　A F D B C E

　　b　**i**　Water

　　　　ii　$H^+ + OH^- \longrightarrow H_2O$

　　　　iii　Citric acid

4　5/6 marks: answer clearly describes the steps for making copper sulfate crystals **and** includes a clearly explained suggestion of why Grace's yield is less than Nzila's for each step.

All information in the answer is relevant, clear, organised, and presented in a structured and coherent format. Specialist terms are used appropriately. There are few, if any, errors in grammar, punctuation, and spelling.

3/4 marks: answer describes the main steps for making copper sulfate crystals **and** for some of the steps gives clear explanations to explain why Grace's yield is less than Nzila's **or** for all of the steps gives brief reasons to explain why the yields might be different.

Most of the information is relevant and presented in a structured and coherent format. Specialist terms are usually used correctly. There are occasional errors in grammar, punctuation, and spelling.

1/2 marks: answer describes some of the steps for making copper sulfate crystals **but** does not suggest why the yields of the two experimenters might be different **or** the answer describes some of the steps for making copper sulfate crystals **and** suggests why the yields of the two experimenters might be different **and** the explanation lacks detail/clarity.

There may be limited use of specialist terms. Errors of grammar, punctuation, and spelling prevent communication of the science. Answer includes 1 or 2 points of those listed below.

0 marks: insufficient or irrelevant science. Answer not worthy of credit.

Relevant points include:

• Add copper oxide powder to sulfuric acid solution, with stirring, until no more will dissolved.

- During this step, Grace might not have added enough copper oxide powder. This would have decreased her yield compared to Nzila.
- Filter the mixture. Keep the solution.
- During this step, Grace might not have waited until all the solution had passed through the filter paper. This would have decreased her yield compared to Nzila.
- Heat the copper sulfate solution in an evaporating dish until its volume decreases to about half its original volume.
- During this step, Grace might have allowed the solution to spit. This would have decreased her yield compared to Nzila.
- Leave the concentrated solution in an evaporating dish to crystallise.
- During this step, Grace might have spilt some of the solution, which would have decreased her yield compared to Nzila.

5 **a** 201 kg
 b 320 kg
 c 490 kg

P6 Workout

1 Alpha: slow down, least, most, most
Beta: smaller, less, further, less
Gamma: least, least

2

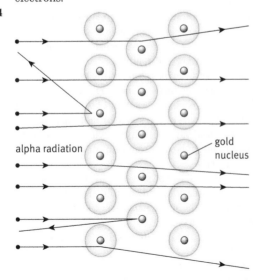

fallout occupational
gamma rays from ground and buildings
medical
radon gas from ground
cosmic rays
food and drink

3 From top: nucleus, made up of protons and neutrons; electrons.

4

alpha radiation
gold nucleus

5 **a** A and B; D and E
 b F
 c E
 d B and C

P6 Quickfire

1 a, b, c, d

2 True statements: **a, c, e**
Corrected versions of false statements:
 b Atoms of carbon-14 are radioactive. If a carbon-14 atom joins to oxygen atoms to make carbon dioxide, the carbon dioxide will be radioactive.
 d Radiation dose is measured in sieverts.
 f Hydrogen nuclei can join together to make helium nuclei. The process is called nuclear fusion.
 g The energy released in a nuclear reaction is much greater than the energy released in a chemical reaction involving a similar mass of material.

3 Irradiation – being exposed to radiation from a source outside your body; contamination – having a radioactive substance inside your body; radiation dose – a measure of the possible harm to your body caused by radiation.

4 Hospital radiographers, nuclear power station workers

5 **a** If the half-life was much longer that this, the krypton would continue to emit significant amounts of ionising radiation after it has done its job.
 b 26 s
 c Wear protective clothing, monitor radiation exposure closely.

6 Neutrons, strong, electrostatic, unstable, decays, radiation

7 **a** 9 minutes
 b 8 days
 c 207 years

8 **a** 92 protons and 147 neutrons
 b 92 protons and 133 neutrons
 c 92 protons and 125 neutrons

9 73×10^{-6} kg

10 **a** Fuel rod: contains uranium-235 atoms, which split into two smaller parts when their nuclei absorb neutrons. The process releases energy.
 b Control rod: absorbs neutrons. Moved into or out of the reactor to control the reaction rate.
 c Coolant: is heated up by the fuel rods, and used to heat water to make steam to turn turbines.

11 **a** $^{239}_{92}\text{U} \longrightarrow {}^{239}_{93}\text{Np} + {}^{0}_{-1}\beta$
 b $^{14}_{6}\text{C} \longrightarrow {}^{14}_{7}\text{N} + {}^{0}_{-1}\beta$
 c $^{235}_{92}\text{U} \longrightarrow {}^{231}_{90}\text{Th} + {}^{4}_{2}\alpha$
 d $^{209}_{83}\text{Po} \longrightarrow {}^{205}_{81}\text{Tl} + {}^{4}_{2}\alpha$
 e $^{219}_{86}\text{Rn} \longrightarrow {}^{215}_{84}\text{Bi} + {}^{4}_{2}\alpha$

P6 GCSE-style questions

1 **a** **i** Radioactive
   ii Gamma radiation can penetrate deep inside Arthur's body to reach his tumour.
 b **i** Kill them
   ii The gamma radiation also kills healthy cells.
 c **i** To prevent ionising radiation from leaving the room.
   ii To minimise the dose of ionising radiation she/he receives.

2 **a** The activity of the Cs-137 source decreases over time; the half-life of Cs-137 is 30 years.
 b 0.625 g
 c Unstable, stable

3 a D, A, C, G
   b Rate, boron, neutrons
   c Low level – pack it in drums; medium level – mix it with concrete; high level – store in a pool of water.
4 a i The bar charts show that, for all states, the activity of Sr-90 was lower in teeth from people born between 1986 and 1989 than in the teeth from people born between 1982 and 1985. From 1986–9 onwards, the activity of Sr-90 increased.
      ii No teeth were collected from children born between these years in Pennsylvania.
   b The activity of Sr-90 increased from 1986–9 onwards, as did the amount of electricity generated in nuclear power stations. So the data support the conclusion.
   c The finding makes the conclusion more likely to be correct. It provides further evidence that increased levels of Sr-90 are caused by the generation of electricity from nuclear sources.
5 a i It decays by emitting alpha particles, which are stopped by the skin. Alpha particles only cause harm if they are emitted by a radioactive source inside the body. (Also, plutonium is highly toxic.)
      ii Two protons and two neutrons
   b $^{238}_{94}Pu \longrightarrow\ ^{234}_{92}U +\ ^{4}_{2}\alpha$
   c About 90 years
   d 94 protons and 145 neutrons
6 5/6 marks: answer describes several ways in which ionising radiation is used in hospitals **and** includes a detailed, logical, and coherent explanation for each use.
   All information in the answer is relevant, clear, organised, and presented in a structured and coherent format. Specialist terms are used appropriately. There are few, if any, errors in grammar, punctuation, and spelling.
   3/4 marks: answer describes one or two ways in which ionising radiation is used in hospitals **and** includes an explanation for each use **but** the explanations lacks detail, logic, and coherence **or** includes an explanation for one use **and** the explanation is detailed, coherent, and logical.
   Most of the information is relevant and presented in a structured and coherent format. Specialist terms are usually used correctly. There are occasional errors in grammar, punctuation, and spelling.
   1/2 marks: answer describes one way in which ionising radiation is used in hospitals **and** gives an explanation for this use **or** the answer describes one method in which ionising radiation is used in hospitals **but** does not include an explanation for this use.
   There may be limited use of specialist terms. Errors of grammar, punctuation, and spelling prevent communication of the science. Answer includes 1 or 2 points of those listed below.
   0 marks: insufficient or irrelevant science. Answer not worthy of credit.
   Relevant points include:
   · Ionising radiation is used to treat cancer by radiotherapy.
   · Ionising radiation is directed at the tumour. It damages cancerous cells and makes them stop growing.
   · Ionising radiation is used to sterilise surgical instruments.
   · The ionising radiation kills bacteria on the surgical instruments.
   · Ionising radiation is used as a tracer.
   · For example, krypton-81m gas shows doctors how gases move in diseased lungs.

Ideas about science 1 Workout
1 A – 4, B – 2, C – 3, D – 1, E – 6, F – 7, G – 5
2 a A and B
   b A or B or C or D
   c A and C and D
3 a 230.4 °C
   b To be more confident the result is close to the true value; to check the data are repeatable
   c Clarise's thermometer is not calibrated correctly; there is a zero error on her thermometer; any other sensible suggestions.

Ideas about science 1 GCSE-style questions
1 a i To gather a set of data from which to calculate a mean value. The value obtained will then be as close as possible to the true value.
      ii It was difficult to know exactly when the end point was reached; any other sensible suggestions
   b 11.3
   c i The first reading of 12.0 cm³
      ii The titration reading was a rough one, which Ben did to get a rough idea of the volume of acid required.
   d 11.3–11.5 cm³
   e 11.4 cm³
2 a 25.0 and 32.1
   b i 32.1
      ii If possible, she should check the result again.
   c i Tillie's data set has the bigger range for voltage values, because her range is 1.5–7.5 V (6.0 V difference between the highest and lowest values) and Charlie's range is 3.0–5.0 V (2.0 V difference between highest and lowest values).
      ii True value = mean = 26 Ω
   d The mean of Tillie's values lies within the range of Charlie's values, and the mean of Charlie's values lies within the range of Tillie's values. So the true value is likely not to have changed.
3 a Lilia could do the whole investigation twice more, recording the number of bubbles produced in 1 minute at each temperature. If the numbers of bubbles in the three investigations are similar, then her results are repeatable.
   b Lilia could ask someone else in the class to repeat the investigation using a different set of equipment. If the other person obtains similar data (the change in the number of bubbles with temperature shows a similar pattern) then Lilia's results are reproducible.

Ideas about science 2 Workout
1 a The average mass of citrulline in water melon flesh is lowest in red watermelons and highest in yellow ones.
   b On average, men have bigger ears than women.
   c For men, ear size increases with age.
   d As the average light intensity increases, the number of foxgloves growing in a 1 m³ plot decreases.
   e As the number of generator coils increases, the voltage increases.
   f As temperature increases, the time to collect 100 cm³ of gas decreases.
2 1 causal, 2 outcome, 3 factor, 4 fair, 5 mechanism, 6 flawed, 7 chance, 8 matched, 9 increases, 10 random, 11 control

Answers

Ideas about science 2 GCSE-style questions

1 a The masses of ester compounds
   b i Amount of water; temperature
      ii So that the investigation is fair
   c i As the concentration of carbon dioxide in the air increases, the concentration of ester compound A in the strawberries increases; as the concentration of carbon dioxide in the air increases, the concentration of ester compound B in the strawberries increases.
      ii Kezi and Sahira
   d The scientist suggested a mechanism for the way in which the extra carbon dioxide resulted in higher concentrations of esters A and B. A plausible mechanism linking a factor to an outcome makes scientists more likely to accept that there is a causal relationship between the factor and the outcome.
2 a Outcomes: of the people who took aspirin, 10 got cancer; of the people who took aspirin placebo tables, 23 got cancer. Factors: for 2 years, 258 people took aspirin every day; for 2 years, 250 people took aspirin placebo tablets every day.
   b There is a correlation between the factors and the outcome; taking aspirin reduces the chance of getting bowel cancer.
   c So that other factors are equally likely in both groups.
   d The suggested mechanism increases confidence that taking aspirin causes a reduced chance of bowel cancer; it is possible that the decreased chance of getting cancer after taking aspirin for 2 years is caused by some other factor.
   e i Smoking, drinking alcohol, any other sensible suggestions
      ii One of: the size of the sample was very big; the study continued for a long time period (20 years).

Ideas about science 3 Workout

1 Statements that are true: c, d, f, h
   Corrected versions of statements that are false:
   a Scientific explanations have to be thought up creatively from data.
   b An explanation may be incorrect, even if all the data agree with it.
   e An explanation may explain a range of phenomena that scientists didn't know were linked.
   g If an observation agrees with a prediction that is based on an explanation, it increases confidence that the explanation is correct.
   i If an observation does not agree with a prediction that is based on an explanation, then the explanation or the observation may be wrong. Confidence in the explanation is reduced.
   j If an observation does not agree with a prediction that is based on an explanation, then the explanation or the observation may be wrong. Confidence in the explanation is reduced.
2 1 A, 2 D, 3 E, 4 B, 5 C

Ideas about science 3 GCSE-style questions

1 a 1 D, 2 D, 3 D, 4E
   b They could not see the nucleus; any other sensible suggestion.
   c The fact that the prediction is correct increases confidence in the explanation; if the prediction were wrong, we would be less confident in the explanation.
   d Energy being emitted when uranium atoms decay; *or* the total mass of the products of the decay reaction being less than the mass of the original uranium.
2 a 1 A, B, C, D; 2 E; 3 F; 4 G
   b Galileo made the groove as smooth as possible to reduce friction.
   c He repeated the measurements many times to check their repeatability *or* to obtain values that are as close to the true values as possible.
   d i He could repeat the test described, but with slopes of different steepness.
      ii The ball would have speeded up more on a steeper slope.

Ideas about science 4 Workout

1 1 E, 2 C, 3 B, 4 D, 5 G, 6 A, 7 F, 8 H
2 Examples of suitable sentences include:
   • Scientists are usually sceptical about unexpected findings until they have been replicated by themselves or reproduced by others.
   • Scientists report their claims to other scientists through scientific conferences and journals.
   • Peer review is the process of critical evaluation of scientific claims by other scientists who are experts in the same field.
   • There is less confidence in a new scientific claim that has not yet been evaluated by the scientific community than there is in well-established claims.

Ideas about science 4 GCSE-style questions

1 a To plan how to find out if the other scientists' work is reproducible; to find out what is already known about the effects of exercise and BMI on hip fracture risk.
   b The Million Women Study research reproduced some of the findings of earlier research.
   c The paper is submitted to a scientific journal. Then a few other scientists, who are experts in the same area of science, check the methods and findings. The paper may then be accepted for publication.
   d To let women know that exercising can reduce their risk of hip fractures.
2 a i So that other scientists can find out about their work; so that other scientists can find out if their findings are reproducible.
      ii The result made other scientists less likely to accept Masataka Ogawa's claim; the result made other scientists more likely to question Masataka Ogawa's claim.
   b i To gain more evidence so that other scientists have greater confidence in their claim.
      ii The results would make other scientists more likely to accept Ida and William's claim.

Ideas about science 5 Workout

1 a How can we assess the size of a risk?
  b What do we need to take into account when making a decision about a particular risk?
  c How might we make a decision about a particular course of action that is known to have risks?
  d What makes someone more willing to accept a particular risk?
  e Why might someone be more willing to accept the risks of riding a bike than of flying in an aeroplane?
  f What types of risks are people more willing to take – actions that have long-term effects, or actions that have short-term effects?
  g Sometimes people overestimate, or underestimate, the risk of a particular activity. What is the name given to the risk that people imagine an activity has?
  h In general, when people take part in a new activity, are they more likely to underestimate, or overestimate the risk?

2 Dialogue boxes might include statements such as:
There are risks associated with mining uranium oxide. For example, radon gas emitted by uranium ore increases the chance of lung cancer. I don't think we should ask people to mine uranium.
But we need to take into account the chance of this happening – surely there's only a small chance of getting lung cancer?
Maybe, but the consequences of getting lung cancer can be devastating. It might be someone's mum or dad who dies as a result of working in the mines.
Yes, but think about the benefits of mining uranium for nuclear power stations. We've got to weigh those up against the risk.
True. But the risks are huge – what about all that radioactive waste getting into the air, water, and soil?
Good point. But the statistical risk of that happening might not be very high. The risk you perceive could well be much higher than the statistical risk, since you can't see radioactivity, so you're more frightened of it.

Ideas about science 5 GCSE-style questions

1 a Government energy minister – nuclear power stations provide electricity for many people; Pete – the extra cancer risk is significant, but there are few jobs in the area and the pay is good; Jake – the calculated risk of his getting cancer is small, but if it happened the consequences would be terrible.
  b The nuclear reactors are shielded from the workers.
  c The risk of harm to those living closer to the power station is greater.
  d Workers at the French power stations, and those living near them, would be at increased risk of harm. There would be less potential harm to people in the UK, since there would be no nuclear power stations. Nuclear workers in the UK might lose their jobs.

2 a Tom is correct – the data show that the typical annual radiation dose of a nuclear power station worker is less than that of a typical pilot.
  b Barbara is more familiar with flying, so her perception of the size of the risk is less than the statistically calculated risk. Barbara is afraid of the invisible radiation from power stations, but perhaps is less aware that flying also exposes people to ionising radiation.

3 a Risks – cannabis may lead to anxiety and panic, it slows reaction times, and leads to coordination and memory problems. Benefits – studies in humans and mice show that cannabis may reduce stiffness and trembling. The answer should include an overall assessment of the risk, backed up with evidence.
  b People may think it is ethically wrong to withhold a possible treatment from people with MS.
  c i Will, Yasmin
    ii Verity, Will, Xena, Yasmin

Ideas about science 6 Workout

1 a

A person or people who identify...	Name or names
...an impact on the environment.	Sharita
...an issue that science cannot solve.	Clarence
...issues that could be investigated scientifically.	Karyl, Sharita
... an ethical issue.	Clarence
...an unintended impact on the environment.	Sharita
...an issue linked to sustainability.	Paulina

  b i

	Benefits	Drawbacks
Extracting aluminium from bauxite ore	Jobs for people in bauxite mines	Red mud waste damages environment; higher energy costs; more carbon dioxide; air pollution causes health problems
Recycling aluminium	lower energy costs; less red mud pollution; less air pollution to cause breathing problems; recyclers make money; less carbon dioxide during production	Some people find recycling aluminium a nuisance; fuel required to transport aluminium for recycling

  ii *Paragraph could include ideas such as those below, as well as an opinion as to which method of aluminium production is better.*
The benefit of extracting aluminium from bauxite ore is that it provides jobs for local people. However, there are many drawbacks to extracting bauxite from its ore, including environmental costs such as the red mud pollution produced, and the production of carbon dioxide. Extracting bauxite from its ore produces air pollution which may cause health problems, and has higher energy costs than producing aluminium by recycling.
Recycling aluminium produces less pollution than extracting aluminium from its ore. The process also leads to smaller carbon dioxide emissions. Aluminium recycling provides jobs. As well as the benefits described, aluminium recycling does have some disadvantages. For example, some people find that recycling aluminium is a nuisance. Fuel is required for the lorries that transport scrap aluminium to recycling plants.

Ideas about science 6 GCSE-style questions

1 a Local people may get jobs; the mining company might make a profit.

 b Local roads might be damaged; tiny particles of graphite might pollute the air near the mine.

 c What mass of graphite is in 1 tonne of rock from the mine?; is the graphite of good enough quality to make batteries?;how does graphite dust affect health?

 d i Graphite dust can damage health, and if there were no regulations limiting exposure levels, companies might expose people to dangerously high levels.

 ii Harm done to people who have been exposed to different levels of graphite dust in the past.

2 a Arguments for: reduces number of breast cancer deaths. Arguments against: can lead to unnecessary treatments which may have harmful side effects.

 b Most breast cancer cases are in women aged over 50. Since the life expectancy in Swaziland is just 32, relatively few people can expect to get breast cancer there. The percentage of people with HIV/AIDS is much greater in Swaziland than in the UK, suggesting that resources would be better focused on HIV/AIDS in Swaziland.

Index

Index

Index